25 Years

BILIBALDI · PIRKEYMHERI · EFFIGIES
· AETATIS · SVAE · ANNO · L · III ·
VIVITVR · INGENIO · CAETERA · MORTIS
· ERVNT ·
M · D · XX · IV ·

Item 4

A History
of the Department of Special Collections and Archives
of the Kent State University Libraries
and a Catalog
of the Department's Silver Anniversary Exhibition

· 25 Years ·

SPECIAL COLLECTIONS AT KENT STATE UNIVERSITY

EDITED BY

Dean H. Keller & Alex Gildzen

FOREWORD BY

Alicia Metcalf Miller

THE KENT STATE UNIVERSITY PRESS

Kent, Ohio, and London, England

© 1993 by The Kent State University Press, Kent, Ohio 44242
All rights reserved
Library of Congress Catalog Card Number 93–31427
ISBN 0-87338-500-4
Manufactured in the United States of America

Library of Congress Cataloging–in–Publication Data

25 Years : special collections at Kent State University / edited by
  Dean H. Keller and Alex Gildzen ; foreword by Alicia Metcalf Miller.
      p.   cm.
  ISBN 0–87338–500–4 ∞
  1. Kent State University. Libraries. Dept. of Special Collections and
Archives—History. 2. Academic libraries—Ohio—Kent—History.
I. Keller, Dean H. II. Gildzen, Alex. III. Title: Twentyfive years.
Z733.K34A14 1993
027.7771'37—dc20   93–31427
                                                                        CIP

British Library Cataloging–in–Publication data are available.

Contents

Foreword

Everyone associated with Kent State University is proud of its large library, which confirms as nothing else could the scope and seriousness of this academic enterprise. Among the library's many fine departments, Special Collections stands as one of the richest and most valuable, attracting scholars, writers, readers, collectors, and the just-plain fascinated from all over the world.

No wonder. Kent's Special Collections, particularly in poetry, theater, and children's literature, reflects an unusual level of wisdom and taste. Largely responsible for that are its two curators, Dean H. Keller (1968–83) and Alex Gildzen (1984–93).

Far more than good caretakers, these two men have nudged, cajoled, even wrestled the collection into its current, very appealing shape. They have practiced sleight-of-hand, dogged willfulness, and charming persuasion, guided always by a clear-eyed vision of what Kent's Special Collections is and might be. Conquering obstacles that would have stymied fainter hearts, they have maintained that vision with considerable discernment, loyalty, and wit.

Blessed by 25 years of creative leadership and by important and generous contributors, Kent's Special Collections is destined to grow even more impressive with the years. How could it be otherwise when the spirit hovering over it, Keller's and Gildzen's, is so wily, smart, and resourceful?

Alicia Metcalf Miller

Acknowledgments

It is the intent of this publication to record the history of the first 25 years of the Department of Special Collections and Archives of the Kent State University Libraries. That history not only includes the books and manuscripts which make up the collection but the people — library administration and staff, faculty, donors, bookdealers, and friends, as well as the scholars and students who use the collections — without whom there would be no collection or any reason for gathering together these research materials. While the compilers of this history and catalog have made every effort to present a balanced picture of the development of the holdings and programs of the Department of Special Collections and Archives, we are aware that not all of the people who worked so hard to make the Department possible could be mentioned or given the credit they deserve. We also had some very hard choices to make regarding the books, manuscripts, photographs, and other material that would be displayed. What is finally recorded here is our interpretation of the Department's history and our judgment about which items should be exhibited to represent our major collections.

A great many people have assisted us in making this catalog and exhibition possible. First of all, the staff of Special Collections and Archives, Nancy Birk and Barbara Bass and our graduate student assistant Brent Kubasta, have been involved in all aspects of the project, and Harry Kamens was tireless and always helpful in setting the type for the catalog. Dean of Libraries and Media Services Don L. Tolliver not only supported the exhibition and catalog but the year-long series of events in celebration of the 25th anniversary of the founding of the Department as well. Jeanne M. Somers, Director of Library Services, read parts of the manuscript at various stages of its development and offered helpful suggestions.

We are grateful for the sound professionalism of William Megenhardt, Lawrence Rubens, and Samuel Tussing of Audio Visual Services, and John Hubbell, Julia Morton, and William Underwood of the Kent State University Press. Since joining the University's board of trustees, Alicia Metcalf Miller has been a generous supporter of the Libraries and we are honored and pleased that she consented to contribute a foreword to the catalog.

Elsewhere in this catalog we have listed those persons who earmarked donations especially for this publication. Without their support, and the support of others like them over the past 25 years, we would have much less to celebrate today.

Dean H. Keller
Alex Gildzen

Date	Name	Address	
		Guests	
4.16.85	*[signature] Michael Keaton Douglas*	Los Angeles, Ca.	
9.16.85	*[signature] Stephen R. Donaldson*	Corrales, NM	
9/18/85	*[signature] Bonnie Gilbert*	N.Y., N.Y.	
4/1/86	*[signature] Richard Bigus*	Berkeley, CA	
		Athens, Ohio	
4/10/86	*[signature] Ashley Bryan*	Islesford Maine	
6/22/86	*[signature] Lillian C. Zevin*	Cleveland, Ohio	

Those who signed the department's guest book in 1985–86 were (top to bottom) actor Michael Keaton, author Stephen R. Donaldson, folk singer Bonnie Gilbert, book designer Richard Bigus, illustrator Ashley Bryan, and World Publishing Company editor Lillian C. Zevin.

A Brief History of the Department

Names fall from the book like rain, the rain of memory. The book has yellowed about the edges. The word "Guests" is printed in gold on the cover. It was purchased nine months after the Special Collections reading room opened. The first guest to sign in was the new president of Kent State University. Glenn A. Olds was so taken with the reading room on the top floor of Portage County's tallest building that he joked he wanted to turn it into his office.

Names fall from the pages of the guest book, sparking memories of the many prominent visitors to the tower. Poets began signing in during 1972: Paul Metcalf, Robert Duncan, Steven Osterlund, Edward Dorn. The following year saw actors: Lois Wilson and members of the Open Theater. In 1974 film director Samuel Fuller signed his name under that of General L. L. Lemnitzer. In 1976 more poets visited: Roberta Berke, Phillip Lopate, Thomas Meyer, Jonathan Williams. Before the decade ended the guest book had added the signatures of Alger Hiss, Princess Ileana of Romania, and the critic who coined the term "pop art," Lawrence Alloway.

The decade of the 1980s brought to the reading room novelist Robert Coover, art historian Richard Martin, actor Michael Keaton, film historian Gerald Mast, book designer Philip Smith, and playwrights Megan Terry, Susan Yankowitz, and Dale Worsley.

Another decade and the names continue, those whose career archives reside in Special Collections, such as Group Theater actor-director Robert Lewis and children's writer Cynthia Rylant, and those who only visited, such as mystery writer James Ellroy who signed his name while wearing a kilt and cartoonist Tom Batiuk who added a drawing of a head next to his autograph.

These names begin the history of a rare book and manuscript department, covering more than two decades. But long before the guestbook, even before the plans for a new library with a Special Collections reading room, there was one name, the name of a person who had the interest, knowledge, and vision to create the climate that would nurture the assembly of rare and special materials and who had the perseverance and courage to set about building a collection that would grow into a department with an international reputation as a research center. The name belongs to Kent's second Library Director, John B. Nicholson, Jr.

Kent State Normal School was created by the state legislature in 1910. Two years later John E. McGilvrey became its first president. He came from Western Illinois State Normal School whose library had been established by Margaret Irene Dunbar. He convinced her to come to Kent to do the same.

Miss Dunbar and her sister and coworker Isabelle were hired in the spring of 1913 and had the summer to catalog the 3,680 volumes that were purchased that first year. As would be expected in a school whose mission was to prepare teachers for the state's public schools, these early acquisitions were predominately in the field of education and related disciplines. The first book to be entered in the Library's accession record was John Adams's *Exposition and Illustration in Teaching* (New York, 1910). The record is dated May 14, 1913, and the volume remains, now safely shelved in the Department of Special Collections and Archives.

The first location of the Library was in Merrill Hall. In the fall of 1914 it was moved to the still unfinished Administration Building where it was set up in what was known as the Atrium. It had a dirt floor and was heated by oil stoves. In 1929 the Library moved to Rockwell Hall which had been designed as a library. There it remained, expanded considerably by an addition in 1958, until its move to its present site.

Kent State Normal School had become a college in 1915, extending its program from two to four years. In 1929 it became Kent State University. The emphasis was still on teacher education but soon individual colleges were established and in 1935 the state legislature passed the measure that would allow the University to grant graduate degrees. New and greater demands were put on Library services and collections. By 1937 the collection numbered approximately 15,500 volumes and in 1945, the year John B. Nicholson, Jr., succeeded as Library Director, the count was 82,000.

At the request of the State Department of Education, a Library Science Department was established in 1946 with Library Director Nicholson as chair. The department was begun to help meet the demand for teacher-librarians and the first classes were offered that summer. In 1949 a graduate program in Library Science was inaugurated.

At least one of the courses offered by the new department, Practical Arts of Book Making (later known as Book Arts), would require that students have access to material that would typically be found in a rare book collection. At that same time the Library began, in cooperation with the Art, History, and Industrial Arts departments, to develop a collection of material on the history of printing and the history of the preservation of ideas and the printed word. This gathering provided the nucleus of what was to begin a full-fledged Department of Special Collections and Archives.

No special or secure space had been provided in Rockwell Library for rare or special material so for a time it lined the walls of the Director's office in the northwest corner of the first floor of the building. As space ran out in the office, a portion of one floor of the book stacks was screened off to provide secure space for the special collections. This space, known as "The Cage," was used for this purpose until the Library moved to the present building in 1970 even though an attractive rare book room was provided in the Rockwell addition in 1958. This room was made for storage and display of material only, with service to the collection provided by the Circulation Department. For a short time before the Library moved in 1970, Special Collections also occupied a room in the southwest corner of the second floor of the original Rockwell building.

The collection grew slowly at first, but John Nicholson reported in his five-year survey covering September 1945 to September 1950 that enough significant material was on hand to mount exhibitions to enhance the Library Open House lectures which had begun in 1946. He was especially pleased to report the acquisition of the Decretals of Pope Gregory IX which was published by Anton Koberger in Nuremberg in 1482 and a double fore-edge painting on an 1811 edition of Thomson's *The Seasons*.

However, it wasn't until 1951 that the Library obtained its first major special collection. Ray Baker Harris of Washington, D.C. had begun to assemble books, photographs, correspondence and other material about Queen Marie of Romania and her family in 1934. In choosing a home for his collection he determined that the largest concentration of Romanians in the United States was in northern Ohio and from the institutions in that area he picked Kent. Among the items he donated were books by Queen Marie, mostly inscribed (including *The Country That I Love* and *The Dreamer of Dreams),* an album of photographs of the queen throughout her life, an album covering her tour of America, another album of pictures of her private residences (many annotated by her), books about Romania, and a music manuscript by George Enesco.

The collection was dedicated at a black-tie dinner on October 28, 1951, in the Kent State Union Ballroom with Queen Marie's daughter, Princess Ileana, as guest of honor. The princess, later known as Mother Alexandra, added to the collection and returned to campus several times before her death in 1992. The collection has been consulted often by scholars who have written biographies of Marie and books about Romania.

The excitement over the visit of Princess Ileana and the dedication of the Romanian Collection had hardly subsided when it was announced that another major collection was coming to the Library. Cleveland businessman Paul Louis Feiss's library of about 5,000 volumes in the fields of English, American and continental literature, history, theology, the classics, and fine printing was acquired in 1952. Nearly 450 books from the library were designated for Special Collections, among them the German edition of the Nuremberg Chronicle (1493), the Decretals of Pope Gregory IX (Venice, 1491), the second edition of Holinshed's *Chronicles of England, Scotland, and Ireland* (London, 1587), the first English edition of Bede's *History of the Church of Englande* (Antwerp, 1565), a Bible which belonged to the family of Robert Louis Stevenson, a copy of Aesop's *Fables* printed by Christopher Plantin (Antwerp, 1574), Sir Thomas Browne's *Urne-Buriall* (London, 1658), a copy of the *Poetical Miscellanies* of 1704 which once belonged to Robert Browning, books by Edward Young and Robert Blair with illustrations by William Blake, Charles Dickens's *Posthumous Papers of the Pickwick Club* (London, 1836–37) in their original parts, and several examples of fine printing by the Kelmscott and Doves presses. Julian W. Feiss wrote that his father's library "reflected the discernment of a fine mind, the inner sensibility of a scholar, and that of a devoted lover of books." For Kent the library not only

Library Director John B. Nicholson, Jr., accepts a book which represents the gift of Ray Baker Harris's collection of material on Queen Marie of Romania from the Queen's daughter, Princess Ilena.

President Robert I. White and Library Director Hyman W. Kritzer speak with Henry Steele Commager who delivered the address at the dedication of the new Library Building.

furnished resources for programs already in place but laid the foundation for some of the research collections to come.

Also in 1952 the Library acquired a collection of 35,000 bookplates from Elisabeth Clark Tyler Miller of Cleveland. Several smaller collections have been added since that initial gift, and a collection of books about bookplates also has been developed. For several years, when the Library published a quarterly journal called *The Serif,* a bookplate from the collection was reproduced, along with a descriptive note about its significance, in most issues.

An unsual gift was made to the Library in 1959. The graduating class of that year presented a copy of a Latin Bible printed in 1475 in Nuremberg by Anton Koberger to the Library, bringing the collection of 15th-century books known as incunabula in the collection to 13.

As the University's graduate programs matured, it became apparent that library holdings would have to develop in depth and scope in order to support them. Director Nicholson began to systematically acquire material that would form the foundations for significant research collections. It became common to receive visits from such outstanding bookdealers as John S. Van E. Kohn, Geoffrey Steele, and Henry Wenning, and Cleveland rare book dealer Peter Keisogloff supplied much valuable material. John Kohn was given a wantlist of American literature which consisted of a marked copy of Merle Johnson's *American First Editions,* and he supplied a large quantity of first-rate material over the years. Henry Wenning specialized in contemporary literature and he also supplied outstanding manuscript collections relating to American expatriate essayist Logan Pearsall Smith and Irish novelist-poet James Stephens.

The year 1962 saw the acquistion of the first major author collection by the Library. From a Florida bookdealer Nicholson purchased a collection of 139 items by William Faulkner, including first, limited, and foreign editions of all but one of his books and magazines which carried first printings of his stories. His first book, a volume of poetry called *The Marble Faun,* was in the collection as well as signed editions of *Sherwood Anderson and Other Famous Creoles* and *Go Down, Moses and Other Stories.* The Library has continued to build the Faulkner collection with reprints, special editions, and secondary works, only recently purchasing a copy of the scarcest Faulkner item, the "beer" broadside. Ohio State University acquisitions librarian Hyman W. Kritzer attempted to purchase the collection only to be told it had been sold to Kent. Four years later when he succeeded Nicholson as Director of Libraries he said he had to come to Kent to finally obtain this fine collection.

The decade of the 1960s saw dramatic changes at the University, many of which affected the Libraries. In 1962 the Ph.D. was offered in several programs, and in 1963 President George A. Bowman, who had guided the University for 19 years, retired and was replaced by Robert I. White who set out immediately to strengthen the faculty in order to deliver a quality doctoral program. White also understood the importance of library resources in this enterprise and began to allocate funds to support them.

To accommodate the expected rapid increase in holdings, more space was needed than was available in Rockwell Library. The center of campus had already shifted from the original buildings along Hilltop Drive to the east along Summit Street. White decided that a larger library building and a new student center should be at the heart of the new center of campus. Ground was broken for the new facility in March 1968. Stickle International of Cleveland was the architect for the library building which cost $9,444,067 for 330,000 square feet of space with a capacity for 1,400,000 volumes and seating for 4,000 readers.

Hyman Kritzer, who had succeeded Nicholson as Director of Libraries in 1966, oversaw the planning of the new building which opened for service in September 1970. He increased the staff, reorganized services, introduced the OCLC system to the Library and converted all holdings to machine-readable form, changed the classification system from Dewey to Library of Congress, and, as charged by President White, rapidly built the collection to sustain the already strong undergraduate program and to support emerging doctoral programs. Kritzer's efforts were rewarded when in 1974 Kent became a member of the prestigious Association of Research Libraries.

Writing in the 1974 exhibition catalog that marked the acquisition of the Libraries' one millionth volume, President Emeritus White wrote, "On some occasions there has been a good library within a mediocre college or university; never, however, is there an excellent or very strong school without a strong library." During his presidency, White made a great effort to see that Kent had a strong library, and Kritzer made a great effort to carry out White's vision. He continued the traditional faculty-driven purchase of books and journal subscriptions, but he also pursued an aggressive policy of acquiring large collections of mostly older material to support graduate research.

In 1967 Kritzer appointed Dean H. Keller as Assistant Director for Public Service and Special Collections to develop areas of the collection in sufficient depth to support research, and two years later the position was split to assign Keller full time as Curator of Special Collections. The Department of Special Collections was created administratively while the Library was still in Rockwell Hall and became a physical reality when the Library moved to its new building. The department occupied rooms on the 12th floor, including a reading room which doubled as an exhibition hall, stacks, a workroom, and the curator's office. At the time of the move poet Alex Gildzen was hired as assistant curator. In 1983 Kritzer retired and Keller became Acting Director of Libraries until the appointment of Don L. Tolliver in June 1984. During his tenure as Dean of Libraries and Media Services, Tolliver had overseen the automation of the Libraries and increased the department's acquisition budget. In 1991, the University Archives, which had operated as a separate unit, was incorporated with the Library's rare book and manuscript division to become the Department of Special Collections and Archives. Two reading rooms were

Curator Dean H. Keller and Professor of Biological Sciences Ralph W. Dexter admire a copy of Howard E. Jones's *Illustrations of the Nests and Eggs of Birds of Ohio.*

Future Pulitzer Prize winning poet Gary Snyder visited the special collections room in Rockwell Library in 1969. He showed Alex Gildzen letters of his in the collection.

merged, collections shifted, staff duties redistributed. The combined department now occupies the Library's top two floors.

Curator Keller established a collection development policy for Special Collections early on. It was decided to concentrate on book-oriented graduate programs, especially those offering the terminal degree. Knowledge of the unavailability and cost of some material also were determinants. With these parameters in mind the Libraries acquired several large collections between 1967 and 1970.

Among the first of these was a group of books in 19th- and 20th-century American literature from noted collector C. E. Frazer Clark, Jr., of Bloomfield Hills, Michigan. He became interested in Kent through his friend Matthew J. Bruccoli who had been a colleague of Hyman Kritzer at Ohio State University. From Clark the department added substantial numbers of books by Stephen Crane, Theodore Dreiser, Nathaniel Hawthorne, Ernest Hemingway, Henry Wadsworth Longfellow, Herman Melville, and Edgar Allan Poe. Among them were the first edition, first state of Poe's *The Conchologist's First Book* (Philadelphia, 1839), the first edition of Melville's *Mardi* (New York, 1848), *The Lanthorne Book* (New York, 1898) which contains Crane's "The Wise Men" and is signed by him, *The Carnegie Works at Pittsburgh* (Chelsea, New York, 1927) limited to 27 copies with a page of Dreiser's manuscript laid in, and Hemingway's first book, *Three Stories and Ten Poems* (Paris, 1923).

Clark and Bruccoli also called attention to the availability of the contents of Charles Boesen's Book Shop in Detroit which the Libraries purchased en bloc. In addition to scarce early literary works such as Boswell's *Life of Samuel Johnson* (London, 1791) and the first English edition of Melville's *White Jacket* (London, 1850), the store's stock included collections of works by Henry James, H. G. Wells, and Aldous Huxley, as well as important holdings in "beat" literature, science fiction, and little magazines.

The Libraries made history in 1968 when Director Kritzer purchased the entire stock of booksellers Clarence and David Gilman of Crompond, New York. At the time it was believed this purchase of over 250,000 volumes was the largest such transaction by an American academic library. Seven over-the-road trailers were needed to transport the 7,100 cartons containing 325 tons of books to Kent. Only a fraction of the cartons were unloaded at Rockwell. The remaining cartons were stored in a hangar at the University Airport until the new Library was available. The Gilman purchase yielded many older books needed to fill gaps in the general collection and hundreds of volumes for Special Collections. Among these were Mather's *Election Sermon* (New London, 1781), Dwight's *Greenfield Hill* (New York, 1794), the first account of the Lewis and Clark expedition (Philadelphia, 1814), Trumbull's *History of the Discovery of America* (Boston, 1828), Tocqueville's *Democracy in America* (New York, 1838), Kendall's *Narrative of the Texas Santa Fe Expedition* (New York, 1844), Frémont's *Report of the Exploring Expedition to the*

Rockey Mountains (Washington, 1845), and the second appearance of Lincoln's Gettysburg address (New York, 1863).

On November 7, 1968, Bruccoli and Clark presented the symbolic 500,000th volume — the manuscript of a speech by Warren G. Harding — to the Libraries. Now, with the 250,000 Gilman volumes, the University was well on its way to its millionth volume.

During the first quarter century of Special Collections the Libraries acquired by gift and purchase nearly 1,700 volumes from Bruccoli's library, mostly in the form of comprehensive author collections he formed while writing the definitive bibliographies of those writers. Bruccoli's effort to gather materials "that make a collection the record of the author's career" is demonstrated by his collections of Nelson Algren, Raymond Chandler, Stephen Crane, Ring Lardner, John O'Hara, and Kurt Vonnegut, Jr., which are now in Special Collections.

Early in its development in the 1960s, the department began to specialize in contemporary American poetry. In 1969 Kent graduate and University trustee Robert L. Baumgardner and his wife established the Robert L. Baumgardner, Jr., Memorial Collection of Contemporary Poetry in memory of their son who was a Kent student at the time of his death. Their inaugural gift was a William Carlos Williams collection assembled by Cleveland bookman James R. Lowell whose Asphodel Book Shop was named after the Williams poem, "Asphodel, That Greeny Flower." Through the years Lowell has been central to the building of the collection, especially in his areas of specialization — modern English, American, and Canadian literature. The Williams collection includes first editions, Williams's correspondence with poet David Ignatow, typescripts of *Paterson, Book I* and *Book III,* and proof copies of *The Autobiography* and *Yes, Mrs. Williams.* The Baumgardners later added to the collection major works by Robert Frost, Gary Snyder, and others.

Also in 1969 the department acquired eight letters and a postcard Hart Crane sent to his friend Charles Harris. A native of nearby Garrettsville, Crane was one of the century's major poets. Fifteen years later Kent's Crane collection would become preeminent when Trumbull campus English professor Vivian H. Pemberton donated the fruits of her years of research. Her gift of 115 pieces of correspondence by and to Crane, the poet's christening gown, and other family memorabilia drew national attention to Special Collections.

This concentration on contemporary poetry continued with the purchase of the papers of James Broughton, a major West Coast voice beginning in the 1950s. Also a playwright and filmmaker, Broughton was a meticulous archivist of his own career. His collection is rich in manuscripts of the various drafts of his poems and scripts. It also includes correspondence with many other poets including Helen Adam, Robert Duncan, Madeline Gleason, Frank O'Hara, Eve Triem, and Jonathan Williams.

Other poets represented by manuscript holdings include Alfred B. Cahen, Cid Corman, Collister Hutchison, d. a. levy, and John Perreault.

To close out the decade of the 1960s and eventually to provide material for the exhibition to mark the dedication of the new facility, the Libraries acquired one of its richest collections. Again due to a "tip" from Bruccoli and Clark, it was learned that the 1,500 volume collection of 19th- and 20th-century English and American literature assembled by Haddonfield, New Jersey, businessman B. George Ulizio was available. The collection was formed in the grand tradition of John Eckel, A. Edward Newton, and Morris L. Parrish, all of whom were acquaintances of Ulizio, and the collection seemed to have been made with Kent's collection policy in mind. It contained first editions and signed copies of books by Louisa May Alcott, Lewis Carroll, Stephen Crane, John Galsworthy, Thomas Hardy, Herman Melville, and Oscar Wilde. There are 56 copyright deposit copies in the collection, including Emerson's *Nature* (Boston, 1836), Whitman's *Two Rivulets* (Camden, 1876), and Bellamy's *Looking Backward* (Boston, 1888).

Other predominately fiction collections acquired early in the department's history were devoted to the work of August Derleth and, to support the research of the University's Institute for Bibliography and Editing, Charles Brockden Brown and Joseph Conrad. Josiah Q. Bennett, the Indiana University librarian who had authored one of the Occasional Papers, donated a collection of books by and about Flannery O'Connor.

The first major acquisition following the opening of the new library was the papers of Jean-Claude van Itallie whose play "America Hurrah" had been one of the most influential off-Broadway productions of the 1960s. The playwright had worked closely with the Open Theater and helped the ensemble to select Kent as the home of its archives. The company ended its decade of existence in December 1973 with a west coast performance of "Nightwalk" which the actors under Joseph Chaikin's direction created in collaboration with playwrights van Itallie, Sam Shepard, and Megan Terry. The truck that carried the company's effects from California to its New York headquarters stopped in Kent to unload costumes and props. Soon thereafter the Open Theater's files began arriving in Kent.

With the archives of the company he founded in 1963 at Kent alongside the papers of his longtime collaborator van Itallie, it seemed natural that Joseph Chaikin would select the University as home for his papers. An actor with the Living Theater before beginning his own group, Chaikin established himself as one of the primary theater directors of the last half of the twentieth century. His papers include letters from Stella Adler, Julian Beck, Samuel Beckett, Eric Bentley, Jerzy Grotowski, R. D. Laing, Arthur Miller, and Edmund White.

These three interlocking collections, which have brought scholars from around the world to Kent, were strengthened with the donation of the papers of Marianne du Pury who served the company both in an administrative position and artistically as composer of music for plays by van Itallie and Megan Terry. Her collection includes the manuscript of Jean Genet's May Day Speech and correspondence surrounding its publication from Lawrence Ferlinghetti, Allen Ginsberg, and Richard Howard.

Other members of the Open Theater have donated materials in the intervening decades. They include playwright Susan Yankowitz, who gave her working papers for the production, "Terminal," director Peter Feldman, and actors Rhea Gaisner, Tina Shepard, and Paul Zimet.

The newfound scholarly attention being paid to the theater holdings of Special Collections enabled Kent to attract other significant collections. In 1990 Robert Lewis, a member of the Group Theater who went on to multiple careers as Hollywood character actor, Broadway director, author, and acting teacher, began presenting his papers to the department.

To honor both Lewis and the scholars who use the theater collections the Libraries established the Robert Lewis Medal for Lifetime Achievement in Theater Research to be presented annually to someone whose life's scholarship has exhibited brilliance, range, and influence. The first medal was presented to its namesake by President Carol A. Cartwright on November 16, 1991.

The inaugural advisory board for the medal attended the black-tie event. A special moment occurred when one of the board members, Gerald Freedman, artistic director of the Great Lakes Theater Festival (GLTF), announced that that company would be adding its archives to Special Collections. Soon after, GLTF's founder Arthur Lithgow donated his papers. A leader in the regional theater movement, Lithgow had led his company in Akron, Cuyahoga Falls, Toledo, and Lakewood before GLTF established itself in downtown Cleveland's Playhouse Square.

Other dimensions of 20th-century American theater are covered by two more donated collections. The G. Harry Wright showboat collection includes manuscripts, photographs, clippings, and scrapbooks brought together by the longtime Kent theater professor who ran the showboat *Majestic* during the summer of 1948. The Andy Purman vaudeville collection consists of vintage photographs and scripts of comedy routines.

Another significant related gift pushed Special Collections in another important direction. In 1971 Lois Wilson founded the Collection of Motion Picture and Television Performing Arts by donating the archive of a career which began in silent film, continued on Broadway and the "golden age" of live television drama, and concluded with her final stage appearance as guest star in the Kent State University Theater production of "The Women" in 1973. Wilson portrayed Daisy Buchanan in the first film version of "The Great Gatsby," had the female lead in the classic western, "The Covered Wagon," and played Shirley Temple's mother in "Bright Eyes." Among the hundreds of items in her collection are rare signed portraits of her many show business friends, including Gloria Swanson, Jean Harlow, and Richard Dix.

In 1976 two prominent film historians, Gerald Mast and James Robert Parish, presented their papers to Kent. Mast was the author of *A Short History of the Movies,* a bestselling textbook which went through several editions and became a classic. Parish is the author of more than 50 books on the movies. In addition to his manuscripts and reference library, Parish also donated a performing arts clipping collection which others have added to over the years, making it a rival to

The reading room of the Department of Special Collections as it looked in the 1970s.

Dean of Libraries and Media Services Don L. Tolliver (r) and the Chair of the Department of History Coburn V. Graves (l) examine a collection of Civil War material donated by Mr. and Mrs. G. William Grissinger.

similar collections on the east and west coasts. Parish became a particular friend of the Libraries by encouraging many of his friends to donate their collections to Kent. Among them are Jim Meyer, former film critic for the *Miami Herald,* and T. Allan Taylor, godson of author Margaret Mitchell.

Another significant film collection was donated by Jeanne Keyes Youngson, widow of Academy Award-winning producer Robert Youngson. His personal reference library, memorabilia from his career, and a large collection of Pathé newsreels bolstered the department's popular culture holdings.

Shortly after the library moved from Rockwell to its new quarters in 1970, Director Kritzer established the Friends of the Libraries. The purpose of the organization was to bring together those with a passion for books and libraries to share those interests, to make the resources of the Libraries better known, and to encourage gifts to the Libraries. Friends received occasional Library publications, keepsakes, invitations to lectures, exhibitions, and receptions, a courtesy card to use the Libraries, and a discount on books published by the Kent State University Press. Friends are informed of activities and acquisitions of material made with their support through a semiannual newsletter which began in the spring of 1973.

While the Friends of the Libraries was intended to encompass all departments and services of the Libraries, it became the responsibility of the Department of Special Collections to plan programs, prepare mailings, issue the newsletter, and provide other administrative services for the organization. In fact, early attention of the Friends focused on Special Collections and provided the department's acquisitions budget.

The leadership of the Friends established two major programs each academic year. In the fall there was a lecture and in the spring an annual meeting which included a dinner and after-dinner speaker. The speaker at the first annual meeting on May 16, 1974, was book collector C. E. Frazer Clark, Jr. Among speakers who followed were book collectors Hugo Alpers, Matthew J. Bruccoli, and John D. Ong, novelist Jack Matthews, poets Edward Field and Jonathan Williams, writer Helga Sandburg, film historian Gerald Mast, printer Robert Tauber, bookbinders Jean Gunner and Phillip Smith, publishers J. G. Geollner and Henry R. Saalfield, librarians William R. Cagle and William A. Moffet, and distinguished Kent faculty members.

Between these events the Friends sponsored receptions, exhibition openings, and readings by Tom Beckett, Jessica Grim, Marc Kaminsky, Jacob Leed, Edward McGehee, Robert Peters, and Henry Van Dyke.

President Emeritus Robert I. White was the first to serve as chair of the Friends board. He was succeeded by Robert Williamson, Edgar L. McCormick, Dorcas Anderson, and William Hildebrand. Membership consists mostly of Kent alumni and faculty. The first count of members in 1978 was 346; today there are over 500 members.

Interests of the Friends were kept in mind in planning the department's many publications over the years. Dorothy Fuldheim's *The House I Live In* (1981) and Grace Goulder Izant's *Some Early Ohio Libraries* (1982) were issued in signed editions for the Friends. A series of bookmarks illustrated from Special Collections books, postcards depicting early campus scenes, and poetry broadsides also were produced for the Friends.

In June of 1978, and continuing for three more years, the Friends sponsored a book fair in the Student Center which drew used and rare book dealers from across northern Ohio. The fair became so successful it overtaxed the Library staff and space resources and in 1982 its sponsorship was taken over by the Northern Ohio Bibliophilic Society (NOBS), of which the department is a member.

The most recent new activity of the Friends is sponsorship of an "adopt-a-book" program which encourages the gift of a book to the Libraries in honor or memory of a family member, friend or colleague.

Because of the work of the Friends, the Libraries have benefitted from many donations. The first endowment for Special Collections was established by Helen Griebling in memory of her husband, Erich T. Griebling, who had served Kent for many years as a professor of English. Income from the endowment was designated for the purchase of English and American drama. When Mrs. Griebling died in 1991, her family increased the endowment and broadened its scope.

Pioneering Cleveland broadcaster Dorothy Fuldheim began to donate her personal archive in 1972. In addition to copies of her television commentaries, the collection includes the manuscript of her book *A Thousand Friends* (1974), interviews, clippings, and letters from Lillian Gish, Hubert H. Humphrey, Richard Nixon, Nelson Rockefeller, and Louis Stokes.

To honor his friend Virginia Glenn (1931–70), "midwife of the human potential movement," Stanley Krippner established a collection in her memory in 1972 which drew gifts from Bonnie Golightly, Robert E. L. Masters, Ira Progoff, Edward Randel, Huston Smith, and Alan W. Watts.

A collection of nearly 100 books and periodicals by and about Edith Wharton was donated by Professor and Mrs. Richard I. Cook in memory of her mother, Helen Scruggs, in 1975.

In the spring of 1978 Special Collections received nearly 700 books and 30 cartons of manuscripts on the history of technology from former Ohio State University Professor William E. Warner, a pioneer in the field and founder of the industrial arts education fraternity Epsilon Pi Tau. The collection is especially strong in the areas of woodworking, bookbinding, printing, and weaving.

Also in 1978 a collection of over 750 letters to Boston editor and publisher Charles W. Slack (1825–85) and his associates was presented by Slack's great-grandson Paul C. Kitchen, professor emeritus of political science. Editor of the *Boston Commonwealth,* Slack was active in a variety of literary, political, religious, and charitable organizations on the city, state, and national levels. He was prominent in the free-soil and antislavery movements, a leader in the Unitarian Church, a member of the Mechanic Apprentices' Library Association, the Boston Arts Club, the Massachusetts Press Association, and many other organizations. Slack was elected to the Massachusetts State Legislature in 1855 and again in 1861 and President U. S. Grant appointed him Collector of Internal Revenue for the third district of Massachusetts in 1869. Among the correspondents represented in the collection are Charles Francis Adams, Henry Ward Beecher, Salmon P. Chase, George W. Curtis, Richard Henry Dana, Jr., Fredrick Douglass, Ralph Waldo Emerson, James T. Fields, William Lloyd Garrison, Joshua R. Giddings, Horace Greeley, Edward Everett Hale, Thomas Wentworth Higginson, Charles Eliot Norton, Wendell Phillips, Charles Sumner, Bayard Taylor, Henry David Thoreau, and B. F. Wade.

The following year Cleveland book collector Harry D. Bubb presented all 26 books written or edited by Philadelphia esssayist and biographer Agnes Repplier and in 1980 Lillian Sokoll gave Special Collections 280 books, 145 periodicals, and a miscellany ranging from recordings to a film about John F. Kennedy and his family.

For many years Grace Goulder Izant wrote on Ohio subjects for the *Cleveland Plain Dealer* and in 1980 she began donating books from her library. Among the subjects of books she donated were Ohio history, John D. Rockefeller, Alfred Lord Tennyson, and the island of Guernsey.

Donald F. Mulvihill, professor emeritus of marketing and transportation, presented his collection of nearly 100 volumes of first and limited editions and signed copies of work by Christopher Morley in 1981. The following year professor emeritus of English Edgar L. McCormick donated a collection of the works of Thomas Wentworth Higginson to the department. Judge Robert E. Cook, a 1947 Kent graduate and former United States Congressman (1959–63), presented papers from his career, including items relating to President John F. Kennedy, in 1984. The same year Mr. and Mrs. G. William Grissinger presented 23 Civil War letters to honor their son John Knox Grissinger upon his graduation from Kent with a degree in history.

The department's history holdings were further enhanced in 1985 when Mrs. Frank B. Queen donated the western Americana collection developed by her late husband, a Canton physician. The 700-volume collection is strong on Indians and exploration, especially explorers Lewis and Clark, and includes books on Paul Bunyon, Kit Carson, and Davy Crockett.

Thomas Richard Wirth was a keen observer of the New York scene. Following his death in 1987, his friends donated his papers which included documentation of the mail art movement as well as letters from artists William Anthony, Brian Buczak, Gerard Charriere, Ira Joel Haber, Ray Johnson, Lowell Nesbitt, Carlo Pittore, and May Wilson.

The acquisition in 1990 of the Robert G. Hayman detective fiction collection strengthened Kent's holdings in that genre. In addition to runs of the pulp magazines *Black Mask, Old Sleuth,* and *The Shadow,* the collection includes work by James M. Cain, Anna Katherine Green, Dashiel Hammett, Ross MacDonald, and Robert B. Parker.

The donation by Helen Kovach Gildzen of her autograph collection added key exhibition pieces in a variety of subject areas. Among those writing to Mrs. Gildzen were gorilla expert Dian Fossey, poet Allen Ginsberg, politician George Bush, baseball star Hank Aaron, and playwright David Henry Hwang.

Few students of the late A. Robert Rogers, Dean of the School of Library Science, knew of his literary activity in Canada where he grew up. His poems were collected in *The White Monument* (Toronto, 1955) and he was business manager for and frequent contributor to the little magazine *The Fiddlehead*. In 1991 his widow donated his collection of Canadian poetry which included the Iroquois Falls pamphlets of Gael Turnbull and first editions of Earle Birney, Irving Layton, and Raymond Souster.

Another gift which came to the department that year was a collection of over 500 volumes of mostly French modernist literature assembled by Stanley M. Guise, a former member of Kent's French faculty. A friend of Ohio-born expatriate writer Natalie Clifford Barney, Guise had done research on Lithuanian poet Oscar V. Milosz. His library was rich in Barney and Milosz titles and books by their associates.

Upon the death in 1991 of Ralph W. Dexter, professor emeritus of biological sciences who had been a member of Kent's faculty from 1937 until 1981, his family donated his papers. This collection represents his major research areas: ecology, the chimney swift, and naturalist Frederick Ward Putnam. Letters to the latter from Louis Agassiz, Franz Boas, and John H. Winser are in the collection.

In 1992 the department acquired the papers of artist Ira Joel Haber, a contributor to *The Serif* who had designed the cover of Richard Grossinger's Occasional Paper. This collection included correspondence from fellow artists Lynda Benglis, Gilbert and George, Alex Katz, Les Levine, and William Schwedler, as well as writers Lawrence Alloway, Carol Berge, Larry Fagin, Andrew Sarris, Anne Waldman, and David Wilk.

Books for children and young readers have had an important place in the department from its beginning. The works of Louisa May Alcott, Randolph Caldecott, Lewis Carroll, Kate Greenaway, G. A. Henty, A. A. Milne, and Robert Louis Stevenson are represented in depth. There also are excellent collections of dime novels, comic books, juvenile series and early textbooks. Library Science professor Clara Jackson donated a collection of foreign language children's books.

In 1982 Kent graduate Cynthia Rylant began donating her manuscripts. Her first book, *When I Was Young In the Mountains,* was published while she was still enrolled in the School of Library Science. She won the Newbery Medal for *Missing May* in 1993.

Three years later, in the first of a series of lectures which bear her name, Virginia Hamilton announced that she was depositing her papers in the department. Among the first to arrive were the drafts of *M. C. Higgins, the Great* for which Hamilton won the 1973 Newbery Medal.

As a result of her research for a book on the Babar stories of Jean and Laurent de Brunhof, English professor Ann Hildebrand persuaded collector John L. Boonshaft to make the department the future home of his collection of over 2,000 Babar editions, translations, art work, and realia. In 1991 Boonshaft willed his collection to Kent with an endowment for its maintenance.

Of considerable importance to the children's literature collection, and closely related to holdings in the history of printing and publishing, is the archive of the Saalfield Company of Akron. It includes mint-condition file copies of its publications (storybooks, paper dolls, coloring books, puzzles, activity books, and games) as well as manuscripts, art work, promotional material, and production files. The company evolved at the turn of the century from the Werner Publishing Company in Akron and was a pioneer in marketing children's books and games through "five and dime" stores. It was the first company to acquire licenses to use names and images of celebrities in their products. The first star they signed was Shirley Temple who proved to be a great success for the company.

Complementing the acquisiton of the Saalfield archives and the department's strength in the history of printing and publishing was the gift in 1986 of a large collection of books issued by the World Publishing Company of Cleveland and New York. The collection was donated by Lillian C. Zevin, daughter of the company's founder and wife of Ben Zevin, the firm's president. World was well known for its publication of Bibles and dictionaries, including the popular Webster's New World Dictionary. The company also published books on such subjects as art, history, music, theater, and book arts as well as works of contemporary fiction and poetry, reprints of literary classics, children's literature, and detective fiction. They promoted Cleveland authors such as Gordon Cobbledick, William Ellis, Dorothy Fuldheim, and George Lanning and brought out such standard works as William G. Rose's *Cleveland, The Making of a City* (1950) and William Coyle's *Ohio Authors and Their Books* (1962).

Shortly after Mrs. Zevin donated her World collection, she encouraged her friend Albert I. Borowitz to consider Kent as an appropriate location for his library of true crime. Discussions resulted in the decision by Borowitz and his wife Helen in 1989 to provide in their will that the collection would come to Kent. However, annual installments began to arrive beginning in 1990. The collection numbers over 6,000 volumes and is focused on the United States, England, and France. It is enhanced by copies of Borowitz's own publications in the field, his manuscripts, and a detective fiction collection, some of which was assembled by his father, noted book collector David Borowitz.

In order to display material from the Borowitz and other collections more effectively, a new gallery was installed on the 12th floor in time for an exhibition to celebrate the acquisition of the true crime collection. In November 1990 the Libraries sponsored a black-tie dinner featuring an address by mystery writer James Ellroy and a preview of the Borowitz exhibition. The following day the exhibition opened to the general public with an address by British true crime writer Jonathan Goodman, a friend of Albert and Helen Borowitz.

The gallery and reading room exhibition space will showcase highlights from the first quarter century of the Department of Special Collections and Archives beginning in October 1993. There have been only two curators during that time. Dean Keller and Alex Gildzen joined forces to produce the silver anniversary exhibition and a year-long celebration involving lectures, readings, and publications.

As they prepared the exhibition and the history of the department, the curators constantly returned to names — names of collected authors, names of donors, names of prominent visitors. One of the silver anniversary activities again focuses on names. As the libraries automated, the traditional card catalog was eliminated. Before Special Collections "dumped" its catalog, a sampling of cards representing long-collected authors was saved. They were sent to the authors to be autographed and have been placed in plastic as paperweights which will be made available to the Friends of the Libraries.

Among those returning cards, Tom Ahern and Aaron Shurin added lines from their poems, Wendell Berry lamented the death of the card catalog, Joe Brainard drew one of his signature daisies, X. J. Kennedy added a sketch of himself nude descending a staircase, Samuel M. Steward wrote a line in Greek, and Evan Hunter signed both his own name and his pseudonym Ed McBain. From Keith Abbott through Paul Zimmer, the writers who responded to this project represent the collecting interests of the department and part of its vital history.

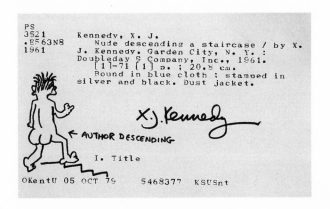

The Catalog

Printing, Publishing, Book Arts

1   Johannes Balbus.
Catholicon.
Mainz: [Johann Gutenberg?], 1460.

This single leaf from a work that may possibly have been printed by Johann Gutenberg was used as an example in *Gutenberg and the Catholicon of 1460* by Margaret B. Stillwell (New York, 1936). The *Catholicon* is an encyclopedia compiled by Johannes Balbus of Genoa in the 13th century and widely circulated in manuscript. It was first printed in Mainz in 1460 and went through several editions by various printers in the 15th century.

2   Hieronymus.
Aureola ex floribus S. Hieronymi contexta.
[Nuremberg: Johann Sensenschmidt, about 1470–72].

This, the earliest printed book in the University Library, is one of the thirteen incunables, or books printed before 1501, in the collection. The black letters were printed from movable type but the initial letters and other marks in red were added by hand. As was the case with most books published in the 15th century, this one has no title page.

3   Hartmann Schedel.
Liber chronicarum.
Nuremberg: Anton Koberger, 1493.

Koberger's crowning achievement as a printer was the *Liber chronicarum,* a history of the world compiled by the Nuremberg physician Hartmann Schedel, which was issued in Latin on July 12, 1493, and in a German translation by Georg Alt on December 23, 1493. A copy of the Latin edition is exhibited. It became a best-seller and remains one of the best-known publications of the incunabula period. This work was printed in an unusually large number of copies for books of this time—1,500 of the Latin edition and 1,000 of the German edition—and a recent census records 800 of the Latin and 408 of the German books still in existence in libraries. Two local engravers, Michel Wohlgemuth and Wilhelm Pleydenworff, probably with the assistance of Wohlgemuth's young apprentice Albrecht Dürer, prepared 645 woodcuts to represent 1,809 people and scenes in the work. Obviously these 645 woodcuts were made to do multiple duty. This copy is from the library of Paul Louis Feiss.

4   Albrecht Dürer.
     Bookplate of Willibald Pirckheimer. 1524.

The celebrated humanist Willibald Pirckheimer, counselor to the Emperor Charles V, friend of Erasmus, member of the Nuremberg city council, translator of Greek and Latin classics, commander of the Nuremberg troops in the Swiss War, was Dürer's closest friend and mentor. This engraved portrait was used as a bookplate by Pirckheimer and it was found in books from his library which were sold at auction in London in 1925. Erasmus was so impressed by the portrait that he commissioned Dürer, in 1526, to produce his portrait in a similar manner.

This bookplate represents a collection of over 35,000 examples in Special Collections. The basis of the collection was the gift of Mrs. Elisabeth Clark Tyler Miller of Cleveland, and it has been added to by others. The collection also includes books on the subject.

5   *Hore beate Maria virginis ad vsum insignis et preclare ecclesie Sarum* . . . .
     Paris: Germain Hardouyn, [1528?].

This Book of Hours was printed in Paris for use at Salisbury Cathedral in England. It is printed on 120 leaves of vellum, illustrated, contains several sections in English, and lists a large number of English saints in the Calendar. Although printed from movable type, this book, and many like it in the early years of the 16th century, was made to look very much like a manuscript.

6   Samuel Johnson.
     A Dictionary of the English Language: In Which the Words are Deduced from Their Originals, and Illustrated in Their Different Significations by Examples from the Best Writers. To Which are Prefixed, A History of the Language, and an English Grammar. London: Printed by W. Strahan . . . , 1755.

In 1747 several London booksellers commissioned Dr. Johnson to compile a dictionary of the English language. They paid him fifteen hundred guineas for the task, and Johnson petitioned Lord Chesterfield for additional support to no avail. He persisted in the editorial work, however, and in 1755 the first dictionary which could be read with pleasure was published. It brought Johnson fame but no fortune.

This copy was purchased in 1951 from the Cleveland bookdealer Peter Kiesogloff.

7   Virgil.
Bucolica, Georgica, et Aeneis.
Birmingham: Johannis Baskerville, 1757.

This is the first edition of the first book printed by the great English typographer and printer John Baskerville, and it is the first book to make use of wove paper that had recently been produced by James Whatman. This copy was bound by Roger Payne, the most accomplished and influential of the 18th-century English bookbinders, whose style is described as "splendid simplicity."

8   William Law.
An Extract from a Treatise by William Law, M.A. Called, The Spirit of Prayer . . . .
Philadelphia: Printed by B. Franklin and D. Hall, 1760.

This is one of the many books and pamphlets to come from the press of Benjamin Franklin and David Hall during their 18 years of partnership from 1748 to 1766. Law's *Treatise* was first published in London in 1750, and the Franklin and Hall edition was probably commissioned by the Society of Friends of Philadelphia.

9   *Biblia, Das ist: Die ganze Gottliche Heilige Schrift Alten und Neuen Testaments, nach der Deutschen Ubersetzung D. Martin Luthers* . . . .
Germantown: Gedruckt und zu finden bey Christoph Saur, 1776.

Members of the Saur family were among the most important printers in colonial America. They issued three German editions of the Bible, in 1743, 1763, and the edition displayed here. There are stories, probably apocryphal, that the sheets for this edition were either destroyed by the British at the Battle of Germantown in 1777 or that, a short time later, they were used by American soldiers as cartridge paper. This Bible has therefore been called the "gun wad" Bible. Of considerably more importance is the probability that this is the first Bible to be printed with American type. In 1772 Christopher Saur II established a foundry which was operated by Justus Fox who produced the "pica" type used for this, the third edition, of Saur's Bible.

10   Charles Dickens.
        The Posthumous Papers of the Pickwick Club.
        London: Chapman and Hall, 1836–37.

This volume of Dickens's *Pickwick Papers* is made up from the original 20 monthly parts in 19 issues and is the most lavishly bound book in the collection. The covers are bevelled and covered with green crushed morocco leather with a red leather inlay on the front cover and with gold tooling on the front and back covers and spine; all edges of the book are gilt and goffered; the free endpapers are of silk and the pastedown endpapers are of red and green leather with dentelle borders, a treatment known as doublure. A portrait of Dickens, aged 27, after a painting by Maclise, is mounted on the inside of the front cover in a brass frame covered with glass. The book is contained in a red morocco "pull-off" box. The binding was executed by Root & Son of London for the London bookseller Charles J. Sawyer, Ltd., and is from the library of B. George Ulizio.

11   *The Babes in the Wood*.
        London: Joseph Cundall, 1849.

Cedric Chivers, a bookbinder in Bath, England, developed a technique of using transparent vellum to protect colored designs on the covers of books. The design is usually a painting on paper which is attached to the boards of the cover. The method is known as vellucent binding. The ballad *Babes in the Wood* is here printed on the rectos of 10 vellum leaves. A pencil sketch for the cover painting by an anonymous artist is inserted at the end of the volume. The book is from the library of B. George Ulizio.

12   *The Royal Kalendar . . . for the Year 1877*.
        London: Printed for R. & A. Suttaby, [1876].

Somewhere between the art of binding and the art of illustration lies the fore-edge painting. The example here shows a view of the castle and town of Windsor in England. Painting on the fore-edge of books dates back to the 10th century, but the first concealed painting dates from 1649 and the art was practiced by the binder Samuel Mearne in the mid-17th century. The binder William Edwards of Halifax, around 1750, took up the practice and popularized it.

13   Palm-leaf book.
        Manuscript. [1880?].

This "nungsu bai lan" or palm-leaf book was produced in northeast Thailand about 100 years ago, possibly by a Buddhist monk. The text is a jataka story, one of the 547 lives of the Buddha preceding enlightenment. It was scratched on the leaves with a stylus and the letters were then highlighted with lampblack.

14   Dante Gabriel Rossetti.
Hand & Soul.
Hammersmith: The Kelmscott Press, 1895.

In 1893 Thomas J. Cobden-Sanderson established The Doves Bindery, originally to bind books printed by William Morris at his Kelmscott Press. This binding, executed in 1904 on a copy of Rossetti's *Hand & Soul,* is typical of his work. This Kelmscott edition of Rossetti's poem is unusual in that it was printed for the Chicago publisher Way & Williams. There were 300 copies printed on paper for distribution in America and 225 copies on paper for England.

15   *The Romance of Sir Degrevant.*
Hammersmith: The Kelmscott Press, 1896.

Kelmscott Press books seem to have inspired many binders to do their finest work. This crushed green morocco binding with blue, brown, yellow, and gray inlays, marbled endpapers, and dentelle borders was done at the Rowfant Bindery in Cleveland, Ohio, with finishing work by L. Maillard and G. Pilon. The book is from the library of Paul Louis Feiss.

16   Geoffrey Chaucer.
The Works of Geoffrey Chaucer.
Hammersmith: The Kelmscott Press, 1896.

This is the most ambitious work undertaken by William Morris at his Kelmscott Press, and it is a monument of modern fine printing. Four hundred and twenty-five copies were printed on paper. There are 87 illustrations by Sir Edward Burne-Jones, and a full page woodcut title, 14 large borders, 18 borders or frames for the illustrations, 26 large initial letters, and other large and small initials, all designed by Morris himself.

17   William Wordsworth.
Poems.
London: The Vale Press, 1902.

Designer and illustrator Charles Ricketts established The Vale Press in 1896 just two years before the Kelmscott Press ceased its operations. Although influenced by William Morris, Ricketts's books were also influenced by the Art Nouveau movement and have a more varied and individual look than those that came from the Kelmscott Press. Forty-six books were printed at The Vale Press, including a 39 volume set of Shakespeare and this volume of poems by Wordsworth. It is edited by T. Sturge Moore who also designed and cut the six illustrations which were used in the book. Three hundred and ten copies were printed.

18   *The English Bible, Containing the Old Testament & the New . . . .*
Hammersmith: The Doves Press, 1903-5.

In commenting on books issued by the Doves Press, Will Ransom wrote that "When it is said that they approach dangerously near to absolute perfection in composition, presswork, and page placement, everything has been said." This five-volume Bible is the masterpiece of the Doves Press. It was issued in 500 copies on paper and bound in vellum.

This copy of the Doves Bible was given to the University Libraries by the estate of Mary J. Williams, a student in Kent's School of Library Science, in her memory.

19   Virginia Woolf and L[eonard]. S. Woolf.
Two Stories.
Richmond: Hogarth Press, 1917.

Two Stories, "The Mark on the Wall" by Virginia and "Three Jews" by Leonard, is the first book issued from the Woolfs' hand-operated private press. This is the first edition of which there were 150 copies with four woodcuts by Dora Carrington. This copy, which is from the library of B. George Ulizio, is bound in dull blue Japanese paper wrappers.

20   Francis of Assisi, Saint.
I Fioretti.
London: The Ashendene Press, 1922.

The Ashendene Press, which along with the Kelmscott and Doves presses makes up the trinity of great English private presses, was operated by C. H. St. John Hornby from

Item 9

BEFORE THE FOUNDING OF OHIO'S first paper mill in 1807, most of the paper used by the printers of the North-Western Territory was made in Kentucky and in Western Pennsylvania. The earliest printing office in Ohio was established in Cincinnati by William Maxwell in November, 1793; in the spring of the same year the Craig, Parkers and Company mill was operating in Kentucky, and three years later the Redstone mill of Jackson and Sharpless was producing usable paper in Western Pennsylvania. An examination of the paper used in early Ohio imprints and for the inscribing of documents and letters reveals that the early settlers of the West did not rely upon the well-established mills of New England and Eastern Pennsylvania for their writing and printing paper. From the beginning of printing in Ohio, the newly-founded paper mills of the West supplied the needs, although not always in sufficient quantity, and only after overcoming almost unsurmountable difficulties of transportation. The delays and disappointments encountered by the early printers are graphically set down in the editorials and notices of contemporary newspapers. In the December 20, 1794, issue of William Maxwell's "The Centinel of the North-Western Territory," the first newspaper to be published in Ohio, a seven-line editorial gives terse testimony of the hardships involved in procuring paper for printing this four-page weekly journal. This notice reads: "Being disappointed in getting of paper according to expectation, has obliged us to Print on so bad equality. We hope our subscribers will consider the great inconvenience that we labour under in procuring paper at so far a distance from where it is manufactured (page 157). Although Georgetown, Kentucky, where the paper was probably made, lies only about seventy miles south of Cincinnati, the overland route, in 1794, was no more than a path broken through the wilderness, a rough, dangerous trail. The difficulties of securing paper for use on the hand presses of Ohio's early publishers are further revealed in contemporary copies of "The Scioto Gazette," a newspaper founded in Chillicothe in 1800. In the issue of this journal for November 13, 1802, the publisher, Nathaniel Willis, displayed minor irritation concerning the difficulty he experienced in procuring printing paper for his weekly newspaper.

Item 25

1894 until 1935. This is the second book by St. Francis that he printed. The woodcuts are by J. B. Swain from drawings by Charles M. Gere and the book was issued in 240 copies.

21   *Journal of the Printing-Office at Strawberry Hill, Now First Printed from the MS. of Horace Walpole.*
London: The Chiswick Press, 1923.

Horace Walpole established his private press, which he called Strawberry Hill, in 1757 and operated it until 1789. The existence of the journal of the press that he kept throughout his life, and in which he recorded interesting facts concerning all but two of the books and pamphlets that he printed, was unknown to scholars until the beginning of the 20th century when its owner, Sir Francis Waller, placed it in the hands of Paget Toynbee for editing. This first edition of the journal was printed by another famous fine press, The Chiswick Press, in an edition of 650 copies. The Libraries own one example from The Strawberry Hill Press, *A Parallel: In the Manner of Plutarch* by Joseph Spence, 1758.

This volume represents a collection of books on the history of printing acquired in 1989 from the library of Richard B. Sealock, a noted public librarian and historian of printing.

22   James Stephens.
The Fifteen Acres.
Dublin: The Cuala Press, 1935.

The Cuala Press began life as the Dun Emer Press, the creation of the sisters of William Butler Yeats, in Ireland. It enjoyed a long life, from 1905 to 1946, and while the press work was perhaps not as accomplished as that of some of its contemporaries, the literary quality of its work was outstanding. It is very much like the Hogarth Press in this regard. The Cuala Press offered several series of broadsides, including this one by James Stephens, illustrated by Victor Brown. "Broadside" is somewhat of a misnomer since most that were produced by the Cuala Press were two leaves of four pages.

The Libraries have a large collection of books, proofs, manuscripts, and letters of the Irish poet and fiction writer James Stephens.

23   R. B. Stratton.
Life Among the Indians, or: The Captivity of the Oatman Girls among the Apache &
Mohave Indians.
San Francisco: Grabhorn Press, 1935.

The Grabhorn Press was founded in 1919 in San Francisco by Robert and Edward
Grabhorn. They specialized in Western Americana, both original work and reprints, and
they did much printing for other publishers. This reprint of a famous and rare "Indian
captivity" first published in San Francisco in 1857 is a good example of their work. Five
hundred and fifty copies were printed with six full-page wood engravings by Mallette
Dean.

24   *The Holy Bible.*
Cleveland: The World Publishing Company, 1949.

In 1945 the management of the World Publishing Company reviewed its extensive list of
Bibles and realized that there were no contemporary American folio Bibles available. To
remedy the situation, the dean of American book designers, Bruce Rogers, was engaged
to design such a book. He selected Goudy's Newstyle type, engaged A. Colish as printer,
and after careful planning and outstanding execution, 975 copies of what many believe to
be Rogers's and World Publishing's crowning achievement were published. The World
Bible is represented in this exhibit by the Prospectus in which Rogers describes the
genesis of the publication and provides details about the type, paper, printing, and
binding. The title page and three pages of text are included as specimens of the finished
volume.

In 1986 Mrs. Lillian C. Zevin, the daughter of the founder of the World Publishing
Company, established a World Publishing Company Collection at Kent with the gift of
her substantial collection of World imprints and archival material. She also joined with
her brother, Julius Cahen, to establish an endowment with which to maintain the
collection and to support the acquisition of material on the history of printing and
publishing.

25   Dard Hunter.
Papermaking by Hand in America.
Chillicothe, OH: Mountain House Press, 1950.

Hunter, the outstanding 20th-century authority on papermaking, printed and produced
eight books on the subject at his private press at his home in Chillicothe. Of the 210
copies of this book, this is number 84, signed by the author. Hunter discusses the

introduction of papermaking in each state from Pennsylvania in 1691 to Tennessee in 1811, and then he finishes his book with brief histories of American papermakers illustrated with facsimiles of the various paper labels that they used.

26 Bulat Okudzava.
Everyone Is Watching Each Other in Russia.
Praha: Lidove Nakladatelstri, 1977.

Jan Sobota, the designer and binder of this "book sculpture," is one of today's leading practitioners of sculptural bookbinding. Sobota relocated in Cleveland, Ohio, from Czechoslovakia in 1984 and is now associated with Southern Methodist University. The binding on exhibit was completed in 1984.

27 *Inangaro: The Legend of the Coconut.*
Columbus, OH: The Logan Elm Press, 1988.

Four artist-designer teams—Margaret Prentice and Richard Tauber, Sidney Chafetz and Richard Brunell, David Macaulay and Ruth Leonard, Eric May and Rod Johnson—interpreted the same text, a Polynesian folktale retold by M. Charlotte Johnson, in four distinct books all contained in a box which was designed by Greg Campbell. Seventy boxed suites of the four books were produced, of which this is number 64.

Artist Eric May is associate professor of art at Kent State University and his book is exhibited here. The Logan Elm Press is located at The Ohio State University and is directed by Robert Tauber.

Poetry

28 Nicholas Rowe, ed.
Poetical Miscellanies: The Fifth Part.
London: Printed for Jacob Tonson, 1704.

Late in his life John Dryden published four volumes of "Miscellany Poems," translations from the classics by himself and others. Four years after his death, his publisher released this volume with work by Dryden, Joseph Addison, William Congreve, and others. This particular copy is from the library of Robert Browning with his signature on the title page. It has the bookplate of Paul Louis Feiss and is kept in a protective leather case signed by fine binders Sangorski & Sutcliffe.

29 Alexander Pope.
The Dunciad.
London: Printed for Lawton Gulliver, 1729.

The success of Pope's anonymous satire in 1728 prompted this second edition the following year with new material, including as a preface Pope's defense of the work published under the name of a friend.

30 Christopher Smart.
Poems on Several Occasions.
London: Printed for the author, by W. Strahan, 1752.

In the year that this, his first book, was published, Smart left Cambridge for London where he made a living editing Grub Street publications. He had married the daughter of publisher John Newbery who brought out this volume.

31 William Wordsworth.
Lyrical Ballads.
London: T. N. Longman and O. Rees, 1800.

Two years after the publication of *Lyrical Ballads,* this second edition was issued with new poems and Wordsworth's famous introduction which blasted the previous century's poetic taste.

32 Lord Byron.
English Bards and Scotch Reviewers.
London: James Cawthorn, [1809].

First edition, second issue. This early work by George Gordon Byron satirized a critic who had been unkind to his first published works.

33 Walt Whitman.
Leaves of Grass.
Brooklyn, NY: n.p., 1855.

The one millionth volume added to the Kent State University Libraries in 1974 was this first edition, first issue of the book that began modern poetry in the United States. This copy is signed by John Chipman Hoadley, a friend of Herman Melville, and bears the bookplate of noted collector A. Edward Newton. It was the gift of Victor E. Buehrle who graduated from Kent in 1950.

34   A. E. Housman.
      A Shropshire Lad.
      London: Kegan Paul, Trench, Trubner and Co., 1896.

      This is one of the 350 copies of the first edition of 500 with the original title page. It has
      the bookplate of Patricia C. Ulizio.

35   Robert Frost.
      A Boy's Will.
      London: David Nutt, 1913.

      Frost's first book was published in England two years before the American edition. This
      copy is from the Robert L. Baumgardner, Jr., Memorial Collection of Contemporary
      Poetry established in 1969 by University trustee Robert L. Baumgardner in memory of
      his son.

36   Hart Crane.
      Autograph letter signed. 1 p. September 2, 1926.

      Writing on stationery from Hotel Isla de Cuba, the poet asks his father for money. This is
      one of 51 letters by Crane donated to Special Collections by Vivian H. Pemberton in
      1985 along with letters to him from his family, patron Otto Kahn, publisher Horace
      Liveright and the widow of the man who built the Brooklyn Bridge. The library had
      previously purchased nine letters Crane wrote to his friend Charles H. Harris.

37   Basil Bunting.
      Redimiculum Matellarum.
      Milan: n.p., 1930.

      Before the publication of this first book, Bunting had published only book reviews. It
      wasn't until later in the same year that his first poem appeared in a magazine ("Villon" in
      Poetry).This copy is from the library of Kent graduate Stephen Jama II.

38   Wallace Stevens.
      Ideas of Order.
      New York: Alcestis Press, 1935.

      This is number 12 of the signed first edition of Stevens's second book.

39   Kenneth Patchen.
First Will & Testament.
Norfolk, CT: New Directions, 1939.

Patchen was born in Niles, Ohio, and moved to Warren as a child. At the time James Laughlin published this book, Patchen and his wife were working in the accounting and shipping departments of New Directions.

This copy is from the library of Edward McGehee whose poem "Ancestral Theme" appeared in *A Vanderbilt Miscellany 1919-1944.* Son of novelist Thomasine McGehee (*Journey Proud*), he taught with Saul Bellow at the University of Minnesota before serving on Kent's English faculty from 1954 to 1980. His papers and many books from his library are now part of Special Collections.

40   Cid Corman.
Subluna.
Dorchester, MA: n.p., 1944.

The poet "designed, planned, and typed" his privately printed first book. The inscription in this copy advises "there is little intrinsic merit in the verse." It is from the library of Stephen Jama II.

41   Gwendolyn Brooks.
Annie Allen.
New York: Harper & Brothers, 1949.

This copy of the book which won Brooks the Pulitzer Prize is from the library of poet-editor Cid Corman. Special Collections also houses the archives of the third and fourth series of his magazine *Origin* which includes letters from Josef Albers, Joseph Berke, William Bronk, Marshall Clements, James Laughlin, Thomas Merton, Alicia Ostriker, Will Petersen, and Kenneth Rexroth.

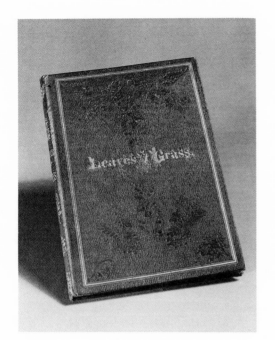

Item 33

TURANDOT
and other poems

by John Ashbery

with four drawings by

Jane Freilicher

Editions of the
TIBOR DE NAGY GALLERY
New York

1953

Item 43

42   Frank O'Hara.
A City Winter and Other Poems.
New York: Editions of the Tibor De Nagy Gallery, [1952].

This is number 25 of 150 numbered copies of O'Hara's first book. Although the title page gives the publication date as 1951, it was actually printed by Ruthven Todd the following year.

43   John Ashbery.
Turandot and Other Poems.
New York: Editions of the Tibor De Nagy Gallery, 1953.

In his Ashbery bibliography David K. Kermani cites the Kent copy of the poet's first book as being one of the few he found which had been numbered.

44   James Broughton.
Notes for "True & False Unicorn."
Typed manuscript. 2 p. 1954.

Broughton was working on this "tapestry of voices" in Paris. It was published the following year in the magazine *Botteghe Oscure* and was reprinted in *A Long Undressing: Collected Poems 1949-1969* (Jargon, 1971). The Libraries purchased Broughton's papers in 1977.

45   Irving Layton.
A Red Carpet for the Sun.
Highlands, NC: Jonathan Williams, 1959.

This book of collected poems (1942–58) was the third Layton imprint issued by Williams through the Jargon Society. It represents the longtime interest of Special Collections in Canadian literature.

46   Robert Lowell.
Life Studies.
New York: Farrar, Straus and Cudahy, 1959.

This was a breakthrough volume for Lowell, in which he moved from the classical style of his early work to the freedom of the late work.

47   Marianne Moore.
        Typed letter signed. 1 p. May 22, 1962.

Writing from Brooklyn to Collister Hutchison in Cleveland, the poet claims there are
three of her and advises her reader never to be resentful. The letter is from the papers of
Hutchison, which the Libraries acquired in 1985. A lifelong resident of Cleveland,
Hutchison had been a friend of Hart Crane in the early 1920s. Harper published a volume
of Hutchison's poems, *Towards Daybreak,* in 1950 with illustrations by Marc Chagall
and a preface by Jules Romain. The French poet's letters to Hutchison are among the
papers.

48   d.a. levy.
        "Cleveland Undercovers."
        Typed manuscript. 7 p. 1964–65.

"i still have a city to cover with lines" levy wrote in his long poem about Cleveland
which incorporates its history, from Captain Perry to the Kingsbury Run murders, from
Severance Hall to Short Vincent. In 1971, three years after levy's suicide, the Library's
quarterly, *The Serif,* devoted an entire issue to him. In addition to Jim Lowell's checklist
of the poet's publications, the issue included articles by Gary Snyder, Eric Mottram,
Charles Bukowski, and Steven Osterlund.

49   Ted Berrigan.
        "Speaking of Love, To Linda"
        Typed manuscript signed. 1 p. [1965?].

In 1965 and 1966 poet-critic John Perreault edited a magazine called *Elephant.* Ted
Berrigan contributed to all three issues. One of his submissions which Perreault did not
publish was this translation of Guillaume Apollinaire. It is among Perreault's papers
which the Libraries acquired in 1972.

50   Sylvia Plath.
        Ariel.
        New York: Harper & Row, 1966.

This posthumous collection, introduced by Robert Lowell, became one of the most
imitated volumes of poetry published in the last half of the century.

51   Edward Dorn.
Gunslinger: Book I.
Los Angeles: Black Sparrow, 1968.

This is copy C of the edition of 26 signed lettered copies bound in natural chapskin. Dorn was a visiting professor in the English Department during the 1972–73 academic year.

52   Robert Duncan.
"Poets and Poetry."
Autograph/typed manuscript. 1969.

Oyez Books worked with Duncan on a book which brought together his program notes for the San Francisco Poetry Center between 1956 and 1963. The short essays covered a range of poets from Marianne Moore and Robert Lowell through Robert Creeley and Denise Levertov. The book never materialized. Duncan's manuscript is from the superb collection of the poet made by Stephen Jama II.

53   Marc Kaminsky.
Birthday Poems.
New York: Horizon Press, 1972.

Kaminsky has had interlocking careers as poet, playwright and psychotherapist. This early book includes a jacket blurb from Joseph Chaikin with whom Kaminsky worked on the Open Theater production, "Terminal." One of the poems in the collection is dedicated to Paul Zimet who appeared in that production and later began a company called Talking Band which Kaminsky served as writer-in-residence. He began depositing his papers at Kent in 1987.

54   Thomas Kinsella.
One.
Dublin: Peppercanister, 1974.

This is number 18 of 124 copies printed on handmade paper by Dolmen Press and signed by the poet and illustrator Anne Yeats. Kinsella visited the Department of Special Collections in the year of this book's publication.

55   Henry Fielding.
       The History of Tom Jones, A Foundling.
       London: A. Millar, 1749. 6 volumes.

This is the first edition of what many consider to be the greatest novel of the 18th century. Fielding's influence on the development of the English novel was profound, and *Tom Jones* went through four editions, about 10,000 copies, in its first year of publication. It has seldom been out of print.

56   Tobias Smollett.
       The Adventures of Peregrine Pickle. In Which are Included, Memoirs of a Lady of Quality.
       London: Printed for the Author, 1751. 4 volumes.

Smollett, along with Samuel Richardson, Henry Fielding, and Laurence Sterne, was one of the leading figures in the first great period of the English novel. The *Memoirs of a Lady of Quality* is found on pages 66 to 237 of volume three of this first edition of the novel. It has been attributed to Frances Anne, Viscountess Vane, who evidently paid Smollett to insert it in his book, a creative method of subvention by an author who was paying to have his book printed.

57   Charles Brockden Brown.
       Autograph manuscript, unsigned and undated. [1771–1810]

Brown was the first American to adopt literature as a full-time profession and was admired during his own lifetime by Godwin, Shelley, and Scott, among others. A writer of "American gothics," Brown composed his four most important works, *Wieland, Arthur Mervyn, Ormond,* and *Edgar Huntley* in just two years, 1798 and 1799. Brown in many ways anticipates both Hawthorne and Poe, both of whom acknowledged his influence.

The critical edition of Brown's work was prepared in Kent's Institute for Bibliography and Editing and published by the Kent State University Press, 1977–87.

58   James Fenimore Cooper.
The Last of the Mohicans; A Narrative of 1757.
Philadelphia: H. C. Carey & I. Lea, 1826. 2 volumes.

The Last of the Mohicans, Cooper's best-known novel, is the second in the series of five books which make up his "Leather-Stocking Tales." Life on the American frontier is seen through the eyes of the hero who is known by several names in the series, including Natty Bumpo, Deerslayer, and, in this novel, Hawkeye. This copy of the first edition is from the library of B. George Ulizio.

59   Edgar Allan Poe.
Tales of the Grotesque and Arabesque.
Philadelphia: Lea and Blanchard, 1840. 2 volumes.

Poe's sixth book contains such stories as "William Wilson," "The Fall of the House of Usher," "Ms. Found in a Bottle," "Ligeia," and "Hans Phaall." It is possible that this is the dedication copy of the book. Poe dedicated it to Philadelphian William Drayton and there is evidence that this copy came from the Drayton family. On each title page is written "From the Author / to Wm. Drayton," but the handwriting is not Poe's. The book is from the library of B. George Ulizio.

60   Emily Brontë.
Wuthering Heights, A Novel.
London: Thomas Cautley Newby, 1847. 3 volumes.

The period of four years from 1847 to 1850 was one of the most brilliant in the history of the English novel. It saw the publication of Dickens's *Dombey and Son* and *David Copperfield,* Charlotte Brontë's *Jane Eyre* and *Shirley,* Anne Brontë's *The Tenant of Wildfell Hall,* Thackeray's *Vanity Fair* and *Pendennis,* and *Wuthering Heights* by Emily Brontë, the first edition, which is exhibited here, also containing Anne Brontë's *Agnes Grey* in volume three. This copy bears the bookplate of the English poet Frederick Locker.

61   Nathaniel Hawthorne.
The Scarlet Letter, A Romance.
Boston: Ticknor, Reed, and Fields, 1850.

Hawthorne's second novel appeared 22 years after his anonymous, youthful first effort, *Fanshawe,* and has become a classic of American literature. The first edition appeared on March 16, 1850, in an edition of 2,500 copies and almost immediately a second edition was called for, which appeared on April 22, also in 2,500 copies. This copy of the first edition is from the library of B. George Ulizio.

62   Herman Melville.
Moby-Dick; or, The Whale.
New York: Harper & Brothers, Publishers, 1851.

Melville's allegorical story of the conflict between man and his fate, set in a realistic account of a whaling voyage, was first published in London in three volumes by Richard Bentley on October 18, 1851, in an edition of 2,915 copies. This copy of the first American edition is from the libraries of A. Edward Newton and B. George Ulizio.

63   Anthony Trollope.
Barchester Towers.
London: Longman, Brown, Green, Longmans, & Roberts, 1857. 3 volumes.

This is the first edition of the second book in a series of six novels that Trollope centered around ecclesiastical life in his fictitious county of Barsetshire. Trollope was a prolific novelist noted for his creation of characters and whose work provides an excellent introduction to social life in England from 1850 to 1880. This copy is from the library of B. George Ulizio.

64   George Eliot.
Adam Bede.
Edinburgh: William Blackwood and Sons, 1859. 3 volumes.

This is the first edition of Mrs. Eliot's first novel, a tale of Methodist revivalism. It is a publisher's presentation copy and is so inscribed on the half-title page of volume one.

65   George Meredith.
The Ordeal of Richard Feverel. A History of Father and Son.
London: Chapman and Hall, 1859. 3 volumes.

Critics of Meredith's third novel found that he had "overstepped the legitimate boundaries of what is known by the adjective 'proper'," that he was on "forbidden ground," that he used "extreme licence," and he was urged to "use his great ability to produce something pleasanter next time." Mudie's Circulating Library boycotted it and it was not until *Diana of the Crossways* was published 26 years later that Meredith achieved general popularity. This copy of the first edition is from the library of B. George Ulizio.

66   Thomas Hardy.
Desperate Remedies, A Novel.
London: Tinsley Brothers, 1871. 3 volumes.

Hardy published three novels before he had a critical success with his fourth, *Far From the Madding Crowd* in 1874. He eventually came to be considered England's greatest regional novelist of the 19th century. *Desperate Remedies,* his first book, was published anonymously and Hardy put up to 75 pounds toward its publication. This copy is from the library of B. George Ulizio.

67   Henry James.
A Passionate Pilgrim, and Other Tales.
Boston: James R. Osgood and Company, 1875.

James's first book was made up of six stories which he had published between 1868 and 1874 in *The Atlantic Monthly* and *Galaxy*. In what was to become his common practice, James made substantial changes in the stories before allowing them to be published in a book.

68   Mark Twain.
Autograph letter signed, to Ulysses S. Grant. March 15, 1881.

Mark Twain thanks General Grant for his help in saving the Chinese Educational Mission in Hartford, Connecticut. The letter is from the library of B. George Ulizio.

69   Stephen Crane.
Maggie, A Girl of the Streets.
[New York: n.p., 1893].

Crane published his first book at his own expense in an edition of 1,100 copies under the pseudonym Johnston Smith. This copy is from the library of B. George Ulizio.

70   Joseph Conrad.
Nostromo, A Tale of the Seaboard.
London and New York: Harper & Brothers, 1904.

This copy of the first edition of *Nostromo* is part of a major collection of Conrad's works given to the University Libraries by Walter and Virginia Wojno in memory of Walentyna Korzeniowska, Mr. Wojno's mother and a cousin of Joseph Conrad. This collection is being used by scholars in Kent's Institute for Bibliography and Editing as they prepare an edition of Conrad's work which is being published by Cambridge University Press.

71   Arnold Bennett.
       The Old Wives' Tale. A Novel.
       London: Chapman & Hall, 1908.

Bennett's reputation as a major writer was established with this book, one of the novels in his immensely popular Five Towns series. It chronicles the very different lives of two sisters. This copy of the first edition is from the library of B. George Ulizio.

72   D. H. Lawrence.
       Sons and Lovers.
       London: Duckworth & Co., 1913.

Lawrence's autobiographical novel was written during 1911 and 1912 and the final draft was prepared in Gargano, Italy, after he had eloped with Frieda. Heineman, Lawrence's first English publisher, refused the book, but Duckworth agreed to publish it on the advice of its reader, Edward Garnett. Lawrence gratefully dedicated the book to Garnett. The first edition exhibited here is from the library of B. George Ulizio.

73   Sherwood Anderson.
       Winesburg, Ohio: A Group of Tales of Ohio Small Town Life.
       New York: B. W. Heubsch, 1919.

Winesburg, Ohio collects 23 related stories based upon Anderson's experiences and observations in Clyde, Ohio, where he lived for 15 years. The first edition of the book exhibited here is signed by Anderson on the half-title page and is from the library of B. George Ulizio.

74   John Galsworthy.
       In Chancery.
       London: William Heineman, 1920.

One of the series of novels that make up Galsworthy's major work, *The Forsyte Saga, In Chancery* was dedicated to Jessie and Joseph Conrad. This is the copy Galsworthy gave to them on publication day, October 22, 1920, inscribed "Jessie and Joseph Conrad / Most affectionately / from / J. G." This volume is from the libraries of W. T. H. Howe and B. George Ulizio.

75   Ernest Hemingway.
        in our time.
        Paris: Printed at the Three Mountains Press and for Sale at Shakespeare and Company, 1924.

        Hemingway's second book contains 15 short stories, most of which are concerned with life in the midwest. The stories' style featured understatement and spare dialogue, a style which was characteristic of Hemingway's work throughout his career. There were 170 copies of the first edition of which this is number 130.

76   F. Scott Fitzgerald.
        The Great Gatsby.
        New York: Charles Scribner's Sons, 1925.

        This copy of the first edition of what many consider to be Fitzgerald's finest novel has the famous dust jacket illustrated by Francis Cugat. Little is known of Cugat except that he was the brother of Xavier Cugat, worked in Hollywood as a designer for Douglas Fairbanks, and had a one-man show in New York in 1942. Matthew J. Bruccoli has called the *Gatsby* illustration "the most eloquent jacket in American literary history."

77   Djuna Barnes.
        Ryder.
        New York: Horace Liveright, 1928.

        The first edition of Barnes's fourth book was limited to 3,000 copies. This copy is inscribed by the author for Laon Anthony and dated December 23, 1928. It is from the library of Kent graduate Stephen Jama II who has given his outstanding collection of contemporary English and American literature to the University Libraries. Barnes was the subject of a Kent State University Libraries' Occasional Paper in 1972.

78   Jim Tully.
        Shanty Irish.
        New York: Albert & Charles Boni, 1928.

        Tully's colorful life embraced such occupations as tramp, farm laborer, chainmaker, circus roustabout, prize fighter, reporter, tree surgeon, Hollywood press agent (for Charlie Chaplin for a time), and novelist, and he had a Kent connection. His first published work, a poem about Keats, was published while he was working as a chainmaker in Kent. *Shanty Irish* is one of his hard-boiled novels of lowlife based on his early experiences. This copy, from the Gilman purchase, is from the library of illustrator John Held, Jr.

79   Nelson Algren.
      Somebody in Boots. A Novel.
      New York: The Vanguard Press, 1935.

This first edition of Algren's first book is inscribed by the author as follows: "For Matthew Bruccoli / With best wishes / for 1968 and / personal pleasure / that Matt should / discover the last / hardback copy in / America of a book / which would now be deservedly / forgotten if I hadn't written / better stuff since / MLA Conference / Palmer House / Dec 27— / '68 / Nelson / Algren." On the page opposite, Algren has drawn a picture of a cat.

80   John O'Hara.
      Butterfield 8. A Novel.
      New York: Harcourt Brace, 1935.

This first printing of the first edition of O'Hara's book is from the library of Matthew J. Bruccoli and is inscribed as follows: "To dear John Hayward / [drawing of an airplane crossing the Atlantic Ocean] / am running out of / space. But how the / hell can I do anything / else when Th is telling / us this story? / John O'Hara / Belle O'Hara." John Hayward was an English book collector, bibliographer, and editor of *The Book Collector*; "Th" refers to James Thurber. The following note is on the back free endpaper: "The page references opposite were noted / by the English Publisher (Chatto & Windus). / They refer to passages considered / by them too indelicate for pub- / lication in England. The bemused / hound was added by James Thurber / in the author's and my presence on / July 25, 1938 / John Hayward." On the back pastedown endpaper are written 43 page numbers, some of which have been crossed out, and Thurber's "hound." Passages on the pages referred to are marked in the text.

Chatto and Windus set type for what was probably an expurgated London edition, possibly in 1936, but it was not published. The novel was published in England by The Cresset Press, London, 1951.

81   Constance Holme.
      Typed letter signed, to E. A. Osborne. July 12, 1936.

In this letter the English novelist, short story writer, and playwright replies to a request for information about her works for a bibliography which Osborne is compiling. The

Libraries have a collection of her books, most of which were eventually included in the Oxford University Press's World Classics Series, proof sheets for five of her books, a corrected copy of a collection of her plays, and a collection of 80 books from what is known as her "bedside library."

82   William Faulkner.
Go Down, Moses and Other Stories.
New York: Random House, 1942.

Beginning with this collection of related stories, many of Faulkner's books appeared simultaneously in trade and limited editions. This is number 29 of 100 copies, signed by the author. The William Faulkner Collection was the first comprehensive author collection acquired by the University Libraries. Library Director John B. Nicholson, Jr., purchased it en bloc from a Florida bookdealer and the Libraries have continued to add to it whenever possible.

83   Owen Wister.
The Virginian.
New York: Editions for the Armed Services, Inc., n.d. [1942–1946]

During the Second World War, the Council on Books in Wartime published nearly 123 million copies of 1,322 books of all kinds—light and serious fiction, classics, poetry, detective stories, westerns, humor, biography, and history—for distribution to members of the armed services. This copy of Wister's famous western is an example. The format of the books made them easy to stow in a field jacket pocket. Former Director of Libraries Hyman W. Kritzer recalls reading these books during his tour of duty in France and Italy.

Item 75

Item 86

84　　Brian Moore.
　　　Judith Hearne.
　　　London: Andre Deutsch, 1955.

Brian Moore's first novel is better known in America as *The Lonely Passion of Judith Hearne*. A review copy of the first edition is exhibited here. Moore grew up in Belfast, Ireland, and in 1947 he moved to Canada, became a Canadian citizen, and worked as a newspaperman in Montreal.

85　　Flannery O'Connor.
　　　A Good Man Is Hard to Find, and Other Stories.
　　　New York: Harcourt, Brace and Company, 1955.

Flannery O'Connor's second book—her first was the novel *Wise Blood*—is a collection of 10 short stories which established her as one of the most original writers of her generation. This copy was given to the Libraries as part of a collection of books by and about Flannery O'Connor by Josiah Q. Bennett in memory of Ida K. Bennett.

86　　David Storey.
　　　This Sporting Life.
　　　London: Longmans, 1960.

The subject of David Storey's first novel, professional football or rugby, was a profession that Storey himself pursued until he gave it up to study art full time. This is the first edition of the book he wrote between 1955 and 1958, during which time he was painting and studying art at the Slade School, University College, London.

87　　Max Weatherly.
　　　"The Mantis and the Moth."
　　　Typed manuscript. June 14, 1963.

The manuscript of Weatherly's major novel is heavily corrected and revised by the author. When the book was published by Houghton Mifflin in 1964, Carson McCullers called it "A skillful tale of terror." Weatherly's career archive is in the Department of Special Collections and Archives.

88 Paul Metcalf.
Genoa: A Telling of Wonders.
Highlands, NC: Jargon Books, 1965.

Genoa has been characterized as a novel in montage, a careful juxtaposition of fact and fiction, history and biography. One notable section draws a Christopher Columbus–Herman Melville (Metcalf's great-grandfather) parallel. The book, number 43 in the Jargon Press series, was published by Jonathan Williams, a poet who has visited and lectured in Kent. This copy is signed by the author, also a frequent University guest.

89 Henry Van Dyke.
Blood of Strawberries.
New York: Farrar, Straus and Giroux, 1969.

This copy of the first edition of Henry Van Dyke's second novel is signed by the author on the title page. For many years Van Dyke has been writer-in-residence in Kent's Department of English.

90 Stephen R. Donaldson
"Lord Foul's Bane."
Typed manuscript. [1977].

Kent graduate (1971) Donaldson's first book was part one of his trilogy called *The Chronicles of Thomas Covenant, the Unbeliever*. It was published in 1977 in New York by Holt, Rinehart, and Winston and was the beginning of a steady flow of very successful fantasy fiction. Since 1978 Donaldson has been depositing his manuscripts and copies of various editions and translations of his books, along with related material, in Special Collections.

Children's Literature

91 William Holmes McGuffey.
McGuffey's Newly Revised Eclectic Primer.
Cincinnati: Winthrop B. Smith & Co., 1849.

The McGuffey *Readers* were the most widely distributed textbooks for at least 75 years after their first appearance in 1836. McGuffey was professor of Ancient Languages at Miami University in Oxford, Ohio, when he was engaged by Cincinnati publisher

Truman and Smith to produce the textbooks. This copy of the *Primer,* illustrated throughout with woodcuts, is representative of a large collection of 19th-century textbooks in Special Collections.

92 Lewis Carroll.
Alice's Adventures in Wonderland.
London: Macmillan and Co., 1866.

Both Charles Lutwidge Dodgson, writing under the name Lewis Carroll, and illustrator John Tenniel were unhappy with the appearance of the illustrations in the first issue of *Alice* and had it withdrawn after only 50 copies had been distributed. A second issue was released immediately and the illustrations were satisfactory. This copy of the second issue is from the libraries of the great Lewis Carroll collector, Morris L. Parrish, and B. George Ulizio, and it represents substantial holdings of Carroll material in Special Collections.

93 Louisa May Alcott.
Little Women, or, Meg, Jo, Beth and Amy.
Boston: Roberts Brothers, 1868.

Alcott's writing of *Little Women* was undertaken, at least in part, to help raise funds needed to pay off the family debt. The book and its sequel which followed in 1869 generated royalties far exceeding her expectations. The story is based upon her own childhood recollections and the four girls mentioned in the title are portraits of the four Alcott sisters. The book is considered to be the first American novel written for children to become a classic. The first edition exhibited here is from the library of B. George Ulizio.

94 Kate Greenaway.
Kate Greenaway's Birthday Book for Children.
London: George Routledge and Sons, 1880.

Kate Greenaway provided tiny uncolored drawings for each day of the year and a full page colored drawing for each month. Blank spaces were left beside each verse and drawing for each day for recording the birthdays of family and friends. The verses were written by Mrs. Sale Barker. The small drawings have been colored by hand in this copy. It has been bound by Stikeman & Co. of New York and is from the library of B. George Ulizio.

95   Robert Louis Stevenson.
      Treasure Island.
      London: Cassell & Company, 1883.

      Stevenson's first and most popular adventure story for young readers was first published
      serially in *Young Folks* from October 1, 1881, to January 28, 1882, under the pseudonym
      Capt. George North. This copy of the first edition in book form is from the library of B.
      George Ulizio.

96   Oliver Goldsmith.
      An Elegy on the Glory of Her Sex, Mrs. Mary Blaize.
      London: George Routledge and Sons, 1885.

      In 1878 illustrator Randolph Caldecott teamed up with the noted printer and engraver
      Edmund Evans and publisher George Routledge to produce two picture books for
      children for Christmas, and the project turned into a series which ran to 16 volumes in
      eight years. Caldecott usually chose a nursery rhyme or some 18th-century light verse or
      nonsense for his text. The books were printed in color in editions of about 6,000 and were
      sold for one shilling. This copy, one of a complete set of first editions of all 16 volumes
      in the series, is from the library of B. George Ulizio, is inscribed, with a drawing, by
      Caldecott for Horatio K. F. Gatty, the author of *Juliana Horatia Ewing and Her Books,*
      and is dated October 26, 1885.

97   Mark Twain.
      Adventures of Huckleberry Finn.
      New York: Charles L. Webster and Company, 1885.

      Although condemned by most critics when it first appeared as completely unsuitable for
      young people, *Huckleberry Finn* has become a classic not only for young readers but for
      all readers. Ernest Hemingway said that "All American writing comes from that. There
      was nothing before." Like *The Adventures of Tom Sawyer,* of which it is a sequel,
      Huckleberry Finn appeared in London shortly before it was published in America. This
      copy of the first American edition is from the library of B. George Ulizio.

98   [Sinclair Lewis].
      Hike and the Aeroplane.
      New York: Frederick A. Stokes, 1912.

      Only 1,000 copies of Lewis's pseudonymous first book were printed. It came eight years
      before his first great success, *Main Street,* and two years before his first novel for adults,

Our Mr. Wrenn. Stephen Vincent Benét, who was 14 when he read the book, said "It's swell, one of the best boys books this year, indeed the best . . . ."

99   Booth Tarkington.
       Penrod.
       Garden City, NY: Doubleday, Page & Company, 1914.

This humorous novel tells of the life of "the worst boy in town" as he grows up in America's midwest. It was followed by two sequels, *Penrod and Sam* (1916) and *Penrod Jashber* (1929). Tarkington signed this copy on the half-title page and it is from the library of B. George Ulizio.

100   Frances Trego Montgomery.
       "Billy Whiskers' Adventures."
       Autograph manuscript, signed. July 1919.

A series of books about a mischievous goat by Frances Trego Montgomery was an early best-seller for the Saalfield Publishing Company of Akron, Ohio. In its early days, the company published original work by other authors, but it then developed into a reprint house and also specialized in activity books for children, such as paper dolls, coloring books, and follow-the-dots. The company was the first to acquire licenses to use the names and images of celebrities in their products, the first, and probably the most successful, being Shirley Temple. When the Saalfield Publishing Company closed its doors in 1977, their archives and library were acquired by the University Libraries.

101   A. A. Milne.
       Winnie-the-Pooh.
       London: Methuen & Co., 1926.

Milne wrote four classic books for children, *When We Were Very Young* (1924) and *Now We Are Six* (1927), collections of verse, *Winnie-the-Pooh* (1926) and *The House at Pooh Corners* (1928), collections of stories, all featuring Milne's son Christopher and all illustrated by E. H. Shepard. They were issued in trade and limited editions. The copy of

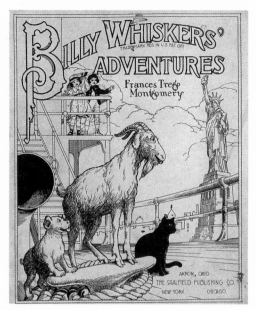

Item 100

Item 103

Winnie-the-Pooh exhibited here is number 318 of 350 copies, signed by the author and illustrator. It is from the library of B. George Ulizio.

102   James A. Braden.
Little Brother of the Hudson: A Tale of the Last Eries.
New York: Harper & Brothers, 1928.

Braden was a prolific author of books for young people, including the popular Auto Boys series. He wrote several books for the Saalfield Publishing Company of Akron and in 1940 he married longtime Saalfield editor and author Alta Taylor. *Little Brother of the Hudson* is representative of the Libraries' large collection of books in series for young readers which was assembled by the Akron collector and bookdealer Roy Van Devier. The collection was acquired from another Akron bookdealer, Frank Klein, proprietor of The Bookseller, Inc.

103   Jean de Brunhoff.
Histoire de Babar, le Petit Elephant.
Paris: Editions du Jardin des Modes, 1931.

This first edition of the first book in Jean de Brunhoff's Babar series and the original watercolor cover for a 1990 calendar by Laurent de Brunhoff, Jean's son, are representative of a collection of over 2,000 books, art works, posters, audio and video tapes, games, and other items associated with the elephant loved by children around the world for over 60 years which has been willed to the University Libraries by John L. Boonshaft.

104   *Superman #1.*
Detective Comics, Inc., 1939.

Superman was the creation, in 1938, of Jerry Siegel and Joe Shuster, 17-year-old youths from Cleveland, Ohio. The comic strip hero has since been featured in newspapers, radio, television, and the movies, and in a long series of comic books of which this is the first. This copy was presented to the University Libraries, along with other early comic books, by Professor Emeritus of Geography Herbert L. Zobel.

105   Maud and Miska Petersham.
        Miki.
        New York: Doubleday, Doran & Company, 1940.

        Miki was first published in 1929 and was the first in a long line of Petersham
        collaborations. It was written for their son and describes a child's experiences in
        Hungary. At one time the Petershams lived in Kent where their son taught art at the
        University. Poet Robert Duncan "grew up on" the illustrations of the Petershams. This
        copy of *Miki* is from the library of Alex Gildzen and is signed by the Petershams.

106   Virginia Hamilton.
        "M. C. Higgins, the Great."
        Original manuscript. 1973.

        In April 1985 Virginia Hamilton gave the first in a series of lectures established at Kent
        State University in her name. She concluded her remarks with the announcement that she
        would deposit her papers in Special Collections. Among the first papers to arrive in
        January 1986 were the various drafts of Hamilton's Newbery Medal novel, published by
        Macmillan in 1974.

107   P. Craig Russell.
        Opera.
        Forestville, CA: Eclipse Books, 1990.

        While these retelling of stories of the operas *Parsifal, Salome,* and *Pelleas & Melisande*
        and two songs by Gustav Mahler first appeared in a more traditional comic book format,
        their reprinting in this elegant hardbound edition is an indication of the growth in
        seriousness and sophistication that is now found in the art form. This is number five of
        325 copies signed by Russell who now lives and works in Kent. In 1992 his work was the
        subject of an exhibition in Special Collections.

108   Cynthia Rylant.
        "Missing May."
        Original manuscript. 1991.

        While a student in Kent's School of Library Science, Cynthia Rylant saw the publication
        of her first book and began donating her manuscripts to Special Collections. The
        department was organizing a retrospective exhibition of her collection early in 1993 when
        it was announced that she had won the Newbery Medal for *Missing May* which was
        published by Orchard Books in 1992. At the reception for the exhibition Rylant was

surprised with a distinguished alumna award from the Kent State University Alumni Association.

True Crime and Detective Fiction

109   Thomas Wontner (?).
Old Bailey Experience. Criminal Jurisprudence and the Actual Working of Our Penal Code Laws . . . .
London: James Fraser, 1833.

This curious work of British criminal history, attributed to Thomas Wontner by the British Library, contains a chapter which describes the work of pickpockets, including a "school" for the training of young boys. The description is reminiscent of scenes in the early chapters of Charles Dickens's *Oliver Twist* (1838). This volume is from the library of Albert I. Borowitz who has willed his outstanding collection of over 6,000 books on true crime to the University Libraries.

110   Edgar Allan Poe.
Tales.
New York: Wiley and Putnam, 1845.

The detective story, at least as we know it today, began with Poe, and in this book, the rarest of his major works, he collected such stories as "The Murders in the Rue Morgue," "The Mystery of Marie Roget," and "The Purloined Letter." Ellery Queen called this book "the first and greatest, the cornerstone of cornerstones in any readers' or collectors' guide, the highest of all high spots." This copy is from the library of B. George Ulizio.

111   Wilkie Collins.
The Moonstone.
London: Tinsley Brothers, 1868. 3 volumes.

This first edition of what Supreme Court Justice Oliver Wendell Holmes called "The best there is" and what T. S. Eliot said was "the first, the longest and best of English detective novels" is from the library of B. George Ulizio.

112   [Jack the Ripper].
"The Murders. The Police Believe 'Jack' Caught. Special Details. Inquest Today . . . ."
London: *The Globe,* February 4, 1891.

This broadside printed over a page of *The Globe* announces what was thought to be the apprehension of Jack the Ripper. It is from the library of Albert I. Borowitz.

113   A. Conan Doyle.
The Hound of the Baskervilles.
London: George Newnes, 1902.

The Hound of the Baskervilles proved to be one of Doyle's most popular Sherlock Holmes stories. He owed the idea and local details to his friend Fletcher Robinson, and it was serialized with great success in *Strand Magazine* in 1901–02. In book format it was also very popular and contained 16 illustrations by Sidney Paget and a striking cover design by Alfred Garth Jones. This copy is from the libraries of W. Van R. Whitall, John C. Eckel, and B. George Ulizio.

114   Anna Katharine Green.
The Amethyst Box, and Other Stories.
London: Chatto & Windus, 1905.

With the publication of her first novel, *The Leavenworth Case,* in 1878, Anna Katharine Green, who has been called the "mother of detective fiction," not only produced a best-seller but a seminal work of detective fiction as well. Her serial detective, Ebenezer Gryce, first appeared in this novel, almost a decade before the appearance of Sherlock Holmes. This copy of her stories was inscribed to Ellery Sedgwick on Christmas Day 1905 by the author.

115   Hawley Harvey Crippen.
Autograph letter signed, to Lady Somerset. October 31, 1910.

Crippen, a physician who was trained in Cleveland, Ohio, poisoned his wife and buried her under the cellar floor of their London residence. Lady Somerset was one of Crippen's public supporters. Crippen was hanged soon after writing this letter. It is from the library of Albert I. Borowitz.

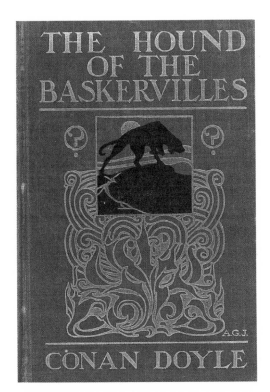

Item 113

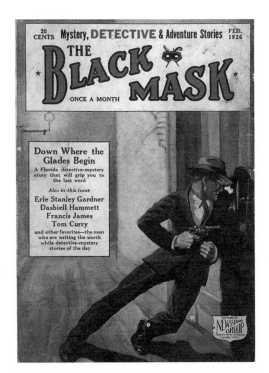

Item 116

116   *Black Mask.* Volume 8, number 12. February 1926.

One of the most popular pulp mystery magazines, *Black Mask* was published between 1920 and 1951. This issue, one of 96 issues in the Robert Hayman collection, features stories by Dashiell Hammett and Erle Stanley Gardner.

117   Raymond Chandler.
        The Big Sleep.
        New York: Alfred A. Knopf, 1939.

This first edition of Chandler's first book is representative of the outstanding collection of works by the leading exponent of the "hard-boiled" school of detective fiction which the Libraries acquired from author, bibliographer, professor, and book collector Matthew J. Bruccoli. A longtime friend of the Libraries, Professor Bruccoli along with C. E. Frazer Clark, Jr., presented the 500,000th volume, the manuscript of a speech by Warren G. Harding, to the Libraries in 1968, and the Libraries have collections of works by Nelson Algren, Stephen Crane, Ring Lardner, John O'Hara, and Kurt Vonnegut, Jr., which were developed by Bruccoli. In 1988 the Libraries mounted an exhibition of high spots from these collections.

118   Robert van Gulik.
        New Year's Eve in Lan-Fang.
        Beirut: Printed by "Imprimerie Catholique," 1958.

Robert van Gulik was a Dutch diplomat and scholar who, in 1940, discovered a copy of a 17th- or early 18th-century Chinese detective story set in the 7th century, translated it and had it published in 1949. The story featured a Judge Dee and van Gulik wrote a series of novels based upon the character. This copy of one of the Judge Dee stories is from the library of Stephen Jama II.

119   Joseph Hansen.
        Fadeout.
        New York: Harper & Row, Publishers, 1970.

Hansen's first novel to be published under his own name is one in the "Harper Novel of Suspense" series. It introduced the popular gay detective Dave Brandstetter. This copy of the first edition is from the library of Stephen Jama II.

120   Leo Damore.
In His Garden: The Anatomy of a Murderer.
New York: Arbor House, 1981.

The murders committed by Antone Costa and his subsequent trial took place while author Leo Damore, a Kent State University graduate, was a reporter on the Cape Cod *News*. His research for this book included over 240 interviews, the study of official and private documents in the case, and visits to locations in the eastern United States and Canada that were visited by Costa. Damore is the author of other works in the true crime genre and a novel.

121   James Ellroy.
"The Black Dahlia."
Autograph manuscript. 1985–86.

Ellroy's novel, which he called "my magnum opus; my most personal novel — my 28 year obsession," was published in New York in 1987 by The Mysterious Press. The manuscript was written entirely in black ink and has been extensively revised by Ellroy in red ink.

James Ellroy was a speaker at the "black-tie" dinner which marked the presentation of the Albert I. Borowitz True Crime Collection to the University Libraries in the Fall of 1990.

122   Albert I. Borowitz.
"The Jack the Ripper Walking Tour Murder."
Autograph manuscript. [1986?]

Albert I. Borowitz is the author of several books on true crime, including *A Gallery of Sinister Perspectives* and *The Woman Who Murdered Black Satin*, but *The Jack the Ripper Walking Tour Murder* is his first detective novel. It was published in New York by St. Martin's Press in 1986. Along with his collection on true crime which he has willed to the University Libraries, Borowitz is including the manuscripts, notes, correspondence, and other material relating to his books and articles.

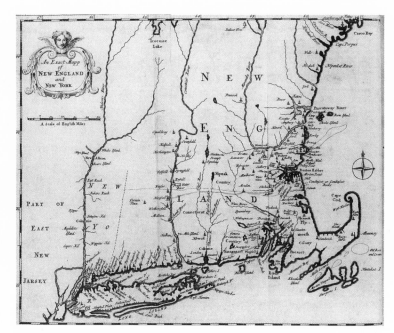

Item 123

Item 124

123   Cotton Mather.
Magnalia Christi Americana: or, The Ecclesiastical History of New-England, from Its First Planting in the Year 1620, unto the Year of our Lord, 1698.
London: Printed for Thomas Parkhurst, 1702.

In the summer of 1693, Mather began to work seriously on what was to be his greatest book and what has been called the "most famous 18th century American book." The work goes far beyond church history, recording political, social, historical, and military events and providing biographies of many of those who took part in them. The book contains a map titled "An Exact Map of New England and New York" showing the territory from Casco Bay in the north to Staten Island in the south and west to the Hudson River.

124   John Hancock.
Autograph. 1765.

Kent's example of the most famous American autograph is on a lottery ticket. This particular lottery was established to rebuild Faneuil Hall.

125   Paul Allen, editor.
History of the Expedition Under the Command of Captains Lewis and Clark, to the Sources of the Missouri, thence Across the Rocky Mountains and Down the River Columbia to the Pacific Ocean. Performed in the Years 1804–5–6 . . . .
Philadelphia: Published by Bradford and Inskeep, 1814. 2 volumes.

This is the first edition of what Wright Howes called the "first authorized and complete account of the most important western exploration and the first of many overland narratives to follow." Although Paul Allen is named on the titlepage as editor, the work was actually prepared for the press by Nicholas Biddle. On February 20, 1814, 1,417 copies of a planned edition of 2,000 were published, but many of these were defective in that they lacked the map that was to have been inserted in volume one of each set. This copy lacks the map but does contain the five other illustrations that are called for.

In 1968, then-Director of University Libraries Hyman W. Kritzer acquired the entire stock of over 250,000 volumes from the Crompond, New York, bookdealers Clarence and David Gilman. At the time this was considered to be the largest purchase of its kind by an American academic library, and it yielded many important rare books for the Libraries' Department of Special Collections, including the *History* of the Lewis and Clark expedition described above.

126   Timothy Flint.
Biographical Memoir of Daniel Boone, the First Settler of Kentucky.
Cincinnati: N. & G. Guilford & Co., 1833.

Flint came from New England to Ohio in 1815 as a missionary and for a time served the Ohio, Kentucky, and Indiana circuit. He moved on to Missouri, then to Louisiana and back to New England before returning to Cincinnati to take up a literary career. This he did very successfully, and one of his most popular works was a biography of Daniel Boone. The first edition exhibited here was followed by 13 more Cincinnati editions between 1834 and 1868. Daniel Boone was one of the most popular of early American heroes, and Flint's book is the cornerstone of a large collection of books of fact and fiction about the pioneer in Special Collections.

127   George Catlin.
The Manners, Customs, and Conditions of the North American Indians.
London: Published by the Author, 1841. 2 volumes.

Catlin was an early and important recorder of the life, customs, and history, both in words and pictures, of the American Indian. His books appeared in a wide variety of editions and issues, and the volume displayed is one of his earliest. It is from the library of Frank B. Queen, a Canton, Ohio, physician and collector of Western Americana, which Mrs. Queen presented to the University Libraries in 1985.

128   Joseph Badger.
A Memoir of Rev. Joseph Badger.
Hudson, OH: Sawyer, Ingersoll and Company, 1851.

Badger was the first itinerant minister, or circuit-rider, to work in the Connecticut Western Reserve. He arrived in the Reserve in 1800 and spent most of the next 35 years there. Badger's book, like so many others in the genre, contains valuable historical, social, and geographical information about the places in which these travelers worked, and they are often the first written records about an area. This book represents a significant collection of such accounts in the Department of Special Collections.

129   Abraham Lincoln and Stephen A. Douglas.
        Political Debates . . . In the Celebrated Campaign of 1858, in Illinois . . . .
        Columbus, OH: Follett, Foster and Company, 1860.

        The first edition of what Wright Howes has called "historically the most important series
        of American political debates" was donated to the University Libraries by Thomas Cox
        who has also presented other valuable presidential material and local historical items as
        well.

130   [Abraham Lincoln].
        *An Oration Delivered on the Battlefield of Gettysburg, (November 19, 1863,) at the
        Consecration of the Cemetery . . . by Edward Everett.*
        New York: Baker & Godwin, 1863.

        This is one of the earliest appearances of Lincoln's Gettysburg address, perhaps the first
        after a rather garbled version printed in a pamphlet called *The Gettysburg Solemnities* at
        the Washington *Chronicle* office. Everett's oration takes up nearly 30 pages of the 48
        pages in the booklet. Lincoln's speech appears on page 40, takes up half a page, and is set
        in type smaller than that used for Everett. The text indicates that Lincoln was interrupted
        by applause five times and that there was "long-continued applause" at the end. This
        pamphlet was acquired in the Gilman purchase in 1968.

131   Christian Cackler.
        Recollections of an Old Settler.
        [Kent, Ohio: n.p., 1874].

        In this rare and important piece of local history, Cackler gives an account of the wildlife,
        Indians, early settlers (including John Brown), commerce, and industry in and around
        Kent (then Franklin Mills) and Hudson. William Coyle called it ". . . one of the most
        valuable accounts extant of pioneer life in northern Ohio."

        This copy of the original printing is in paper wrappers. Another copy in the collection
        belonged to the Cackler family and was presented to the Libraries in 1969 by Mrs.
        Margaret Cackler. A third copy was donated by Mrs. Paul Season.

132   Herbert Hoover.
        Typed letter signed. 1 p. June 21, 1928.

        The president-to-be thanks his Stanford University classmate William J. Neidig for his
        letter of congratulations.

The letter is from the papers of Neidig, who in 1906 became the first American nominated for the Nobel Prize in Literature. A friend of Jack London, Neidig was the author of popular detective stories and the novel *The Fire Flingers* which was made into a silent film.

133   Haniel Long.
        Interlinear to Cabeza de Vaca: His Relation to the Journey from Florida to the Pacific,
        1528-1536.
        Santa Fe, NM: Writers' Editions, 1936.

Reading between the lines, as it were, of Cabeza de Vaca's account of his eight-year journey on foot across America, Long "imagines Nunez relating his experiences to-day, and brings into the open an inward history imbedded in the original but not at once apparent." This copy of the book is from the library of Arthur E. DuBois, a former professor of English at Kent State University whose library now forms part of our collection. It is inscribed to him by Long.

134   J. Edgar Hoover.
        Typed letter signed. 1 p. May 27, 1942.

One of the most powerful men in America, Hoover was the longtime director of the Federal Bureau of Investigation. In this letter he congratulates Ray Baker Harris on his Queen Marie collection.

135   John F. Kennedy.
        Typed letter signed. 1 p. October 19, 1960.

Three weeks before the presidential election the Massachusetts senator wrote to Kent graduate Robert E. Cook, who was running for a seat in the House of Representatives, seeking his support. The letter is among materials presented to the Libraries by Judge Cook in 1984.

136   Harry S. Truman.
        Autograph. June 24, 1966.

This leaflet from The Harry S. Truman Library in Independence, Missouri, was inscribed by the former president for Harold Schwartz. It is part of a collection of presidential autographs which Kent State University Professor Emeritus of History Schwartz presented to the University Libraries in 1990. The collection contains the autographs of 25 presidents including Madison, Jackson, Lincoln, Grant, Wilson, and Kennedy.

137   Bill Clinton.
       Autograph. 1988.

       The then-governor of Arkansas added his signature to the Helen Kovach Gildzen Autograph Collection in 1988. It is one of 2,000 autographs Mrs. Gildzen donated to Special Collections in 1992. Among those who signed cards for the donor were Maya Angelou, Francis Bacon, Benazir Bhutto, Spike Lee, Thurgood Marshall, Salmon Rushdie, and Elie Wiesel.

Film

138   Vachel Lindsay.
       The Art of the Moving Picture.
       New York: Macmillan, 1915.

       This seminal work was described in the W.P.A.'s classic bibliography, *The Film Index,* as a "poet's testament to the motion picture, consisting of analysis, appreciation, and apocalypse: literal, naive, and loving."

139   Pearl White.
       Just Me.
       New York: George H. Doran, 1919.

       White, called "queen of the serials," was one of the earliest movie stars to write an autobiography. This one is notorious for its inaccuracies.

140   *Photoplay Magazine* Volume 17, number 6. May 1920.
       Cover: Pastel portrait of Clara Kimball Young by Rolf Armstrong.

       Edited by James R. Quirk, *Photoplay* provides more than mere "fan" information about the early days of Hollywood. Contributors to this issue include Burns Mantle and Adela Rogers St. John. A run of the magazine from the silent era was part of the research library of Academy Award-winning producer Robert Youngson donated in 1982 by his widow Jeanne Keyes Youngson along with more than 1,000 Warner Pathé newsreels.

141   Silk scarf. [1925?]

       The scarf features advertisements for prominent silent features from Paramount. It is inscribed to one of the studio's major stars, Lois Wilson, "from her Oklahoma Rustlers."

Wilson made her motion picture debut in the only film made by legendary dancer Anna Pavlova, "The Dumb Girl of Portici." Her most popular silent films were "The Covered Wagon" and "The Great Gatsby." Today she is best remembered for her performance in the title role of William C. deMille's "Miss Lulu Bett." Wilson was invited to the Kent campus in 1971 to participate in a silent screen seminar sponsored by the Artist-Lecture Series. Later she donated her papers to Special Collections which she served as a member of the advisory board of the Friends of the Libraries.

142   Terry Ramsaye.
        A Million and One Nights: A History of the Motion Picture.
        New York: Simon and Schuster, 1926. 2 volumes.

        This edition of 327 copies was signed by Thomas A. Edison and the author.

        For years this was the definitive history of film.

143   Cary Grant portrait circa 1930.

        Photographed by James Hargis Connelly of Chicago, Grant's portrait is signed with his real name, Archie Leach, which he used as a stage actor before his motion picture debut in 1931 in the short, "Singapore Sue." It is one of hundreds of autographed photographs of actors from the collection of Kent graduate Albert J. Flogge which he donated in 1993.

144   Welford Beaton.
        Know Your Movies: The Theory and Practice of Motion Picture Production.
        Hollywood: Howard Hill, 1932.

        With a foreword by Cecil B. DeMille.

        Gift of Kent graduate Frank Klein, proprietor of The Bookseller, Inc., Akron.

145   "The Mad Ghoul."

        Press book for the Realart re-release of the 1943 horror film which starred Turhan Bey and Evelyn Ankers. This is one of 400 pressbooks and more than 4,000 movie stills donated in 1982 by Alvin H. Marill, author of *Movies Made for Television* (1980).

At the height of her silent screen career (see item 141), Lois Wilson was photographed by Russell Ball.

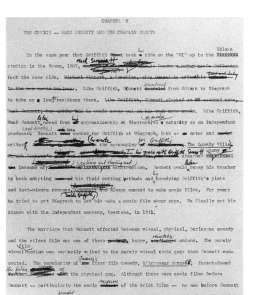

Item 151

146　*Daniel Blum's Screen World 1949.*
New York: Greenberg, 1950.

The first volume in the annual series that documents the casts of all American and selected foreign films. This copy is from the library of Robert Youngson.

147　V. J. Jerome.
The Negro in Hollywood Films.
New York: Masses & Mainstream, 1950.

Inscribed by the author.

148　Daniel Blum.
A Pictorial History of the Silent Screen.
New York: Grosset & Dunlap, 1953.

This copy, donated by Kent graduate Alex Gildzen in memory of actress May McAvoy, has been signed by 21 silent screen stars. It is open to pages 236, autographed by Gertrude Astor, and 237, autographed by Leatrice Joy.

149　Marilyn Monroe.
Typed document signed. November 1960.

A legal document which in effect fired the actress' husband, playwright Arthur Miller, as vice president of Marilyn Monroe Productions, Inc. Gift of Albert J. Flogge.

150　Andrew Sarris.
The American Cinema: Directors and Directions 1929–1968.
New York: E. P. Dutton, 1968.

Sarris, film critic for the *Village Voice*, adapted for American movies the French auteur theory in which the director is considered the author of a film. From the library of film chronicler James Robert Parish who began donating his personal reference library and manuscripts in 1976.

151　Gerald Mast.
"A Short History of the Movies."
Typed manuscript. 306 [i.e., 318] p.

Former child actor and movie extra, Mast published the first edition of *A Short History of the Movies* in 1971. It quickly became a standard reference work and a textbook in film appreciation classes. Expanded editions appeared in 1976, 1981, and 1986. Mast, also the author of *The Comic Mind* (1973), began donating his manuscripts in 1976 and gave an illustrated lecture on Fred Astaire to the Friends of the Libraries in 1987, the year before his death.

152   "The Thief Who Came To Dinner."

The revised final script by Walter Hill of the 1973 Bud Yorkin film. Gift of Austin Pendleton who played the role of Zukovsky.

153   James Robert Parish.
       "The Paramount Pretties."
       Typed manuscript. 794 p.

The manuscript is open to the chapter on Sylvia Sidney, who performed at the University in 1974. *The Paramount Pretties* was published by Arlington House in 1972.

154   Whitney Stine.
       Mother Goddam: The Story of the Career of Bette Davis.
       New York: Hawthorn, 1974.

Gift of Lois Wilson, who played Davis's mother in "Seed" (1931), this copy is inscribed by the subject, "For Lois / My love to the first motion picture star I ever worked with. / Bette."

155   Clipping File: Lila Lee.

When James Robert Parish donated his papers in 1976, 14 file boxes of clippings were among materials sent to Kent. This became the seed for a performing arts clipping file which would be used by biographers and researchers from around the country.

In its first decade of growth, Parish continued to send boxes of clippings to which generous additions were made by Sharon Fox, Alex Gildzen, Helen Kovach Gildzen, Ira Joel Haber, and Jim Meyer.

Representing the collection is the file for Lila Lee, leading lady to Rudolph Valentino, Wallace Reid, and Lon Chaney. She and her first husband, actor-director James Kirkwood, were the parents of a son Jim who gave up an acting career to become a best-selling novelist (*There Must Be A Pony*) and Pulitzer Prize-winning playwright ("A Chorus Line").

156 Beaumont and Fletcher.
Fifty Comedies and Tragedies Written by Francis Beaumont and John Fletcher, Gentlemen.
London: Printed by J. MaCock for John Martyn, Henry Herington, Richard Marriot, 1679.

The second folio of the playwriting team includes commendatory verses by Ben Jonson, Edward Waller, and others. This copy has the bookplates of Algernon Capell and Steven St. Clair.

157 Francesco Ficoroni.
Dissertatio de larvis scenicis, et figuris comicis antiquorum Romamorum, ex italica in latinam linguam versa.
Rome: Typis Antonii de Rubeis, 1750.

An important work on Roman theater, Ficoroni's *Dissertatio* is frequently cited in Allardyce Nicoll's *Masks, Mimes and Miracles* (1931).

158 George Colman the Younger.
Autograph letter signed. 2 p. June 30, 1812.

Like his father before him, George Colman the Younger was a successful playwright whose work included "The Iron Chest" (1796) and "John Bull, or, An Englishman's Fireside" (1803). He succeeded his father as manager of the Haymarket Theatre. In this letter to Richard Jones, Colman discusses the production of "Novelties." It is from the papers of Howard P. Vincent, whose Harvard thesis was "The Life and Writings of George Colman the Younger," and who published an article on Colman in 1936. Later Vincent became a prominent Melville scholar and Kent State University's first University Professor.

159   A. B. French.
"Log Book for 1886-78 [*sic*] for the *New Sensation Show*."
A typical entry in this manuscript showboat log is that of May 25 1887:

> "Amos Papworth went home
> poor Amos is almost
> gone A wreck from whisky
> Got pump repaired
> of Mr. Cha's Rodgers
> price 46 - make bargains
> looked at the 'Geneva'
> for a show Boat
> Sent to 'Farr & Traft'
> Ohio St Buffalo NY
> for best 31 Tow wheel"

From the showboat collection of G. Harry Wright, a member of Kent's theater faculty for 30 years. In the summer of 1946 Wright and his students performed on the showboat Majestic along the Ohio and Kanawha Rivers. Three and a half years after Wright's death in 1964 the University named a residence hall after him.

160   Henrik Ibsen.
Hedda Gabler: Skuespil I Fire Akter.
Copenhagen: Gyldendalske Boghandels Forlog, 1890.

The idea for "Hedda Gabler" came in the fall of 1889 although Ibsen didn't begin to flesh out the play until the following summer. Gyldendal published 10,000 copies of the play on December 16, 1890. It met a hostile press. Ibsen attended its world premiere on the last day of January 1891 in Munich where the play was hissed. This copy was purchased in memory of Melvyn Feinberg, dean of the Honors College.

161   Bert C. Rawley.
Uncle Jed's Fidelity; or, The Returned Cowboy: A Comedy Drama in Three Acts.
Clyde, OH: Ames Publishing Co., 1898.

A major publisher of plays for amateur productions, Ames brought out 491 scripts between 1870 and 1917. The company's founder, Albert D. Ames, also supplied makeup and wigs, toured in productions of plays in which he acted, and published six of his own plays. Rawley was one of the company's popular playwrights, represented by 12 plays, including "Deacon Jones' Wife's Ghost" and "Stupid Cupid."

162   Howard Thurston.

A ten of diamonds signed by the famous magician on November 30, 1911. Thurston, known as "the principal American illusionist," toured extensively. He signed the playing card for Leila Shaw while in Cleveland. The Shaw collection includes the signatures of such theatrical notables of the day as Margaret Anglin, Blanche Bates, Billie Burke, Julian Eltinge, Dustin Farnum, Anna Held, Doris Keane, and Nance O'Neill.

163   Vaudeville Program.

The August 3, 1913 program for Hammerstein's Roof Garden and Victoria Theatre contains this notice: "Mr. Hammerstein wishes to announce that the Sunday Performances are given to conform with the Sunday Concert Law, necessitating some changes in the Program from the regular weekly bills." Among the performers listed is Winsor McCay, the cartoonist ("Little Nemo") and early film animator ("Gertie the Dinosaur") who between 1906 and 1917 was a vaudeville regular who drew "lightning sketches."

The program is open to the announcement of the next week's performers. The headliner is Evelyn Nesbit Thaw in her "First Public Professional Appearance in America." Known as "the girl in the red velvet swing," Evelyn Nesbit was a popular model who became the mistress of architect Stanford White. Later her jealous husband Harry K. Thaw murdered White. At the bottom of the bill is "Popular Comedienne" May [*sic*] West.

This item was one of 1,500 historic playbills collected by Ernest Burns which the Library acquired in 1988. Other contributors to the large collection of theater programs have been Albert Flogge, Stanley Garfinkel, Dennis Hearn, Dotty Lane, James Robert Parish, Harold M. Schwartz, and Thelma Sharp.

164   William Winter.
The Life of David Belasco.
New York : Moffat, Yard and Co., 1918. 2 volumes.

This set is inscribed by Broadway producer Belasco to Peggy Lee (Tufford Hillmer), sister of Lila Lee. Hillmer appeared on Broadway opposite Al Jolson and in a silent movie starring Wallace Beery before moving to Elyria, Ohio. For a while she took care of her nephew Jim Kirkwood who dedicated his novel *Hit Me With A Rainbow* (1980) to her. Hillmer gave this set to Alex Gildzen while he was attending Elyria High School.

165   Laurette Taylor.
"The Greatest of These —": A Diary With Portraits of the Patriotic All-Star Tour of "Out There."
New York: George H. Doran, 1918.

One of the great actresses of the American stage, Taylor is best known today for having originated the role of Amanda Wingfield in "The Glass Menagerie." This copy, inscribed by Taylor to George B. Kauffman, is from the library of critic and theater historian John Gassner. It was presented by Fred and Marilyn DuBois with other books from the Gassner library.

166   Eugene O'Neill.
Autograph letter signed. 1 p. November 19, 1919.

The young playwright gives Pierre Loving permission to publish a play of his in *Fifty Contemporary One-Act Plays* (Cincinnati, 1921). In a postscript he reveals that his best one-act play is "The Moon of the Caribbees."

167   Eva Allen Alberti.
A Handbook of Acting: Based on The New Pantomime.
New York: Samuel French, 1932.

Madame Alberti inscribed this copy to actor Frederic March. It has the bookplate of March and his wife, actress Florence Eldridge, and was purchased from Gilman's.

168   Karl Keller.
"Life Mask of David Wayne" (1934).

This mask was made two years before Wayne's stage debut in a Cleveland production of "As You Like It." His long acting career includes appearances in the Broadway hits, "Finian's Rainbow" (1947), "Mr. Roberts" (1948), "Teahouse of the August Moon" (1953), "Say Darling" (1958) and "After the Fall" (1964). It is the gift of Charles R. Walker who encouraged Wayne early in his career.

169   Andy Purman.
"That's Good — That's Bad"
Typed manuscript. 1 p. [1935?]

Andrew F. Purman was born at the turn of the century. He was wounded while serving in France during World War I. Upon his return, he toured the midwest in minstrel shows. In the 1930s he wrote and appeared on the Canadian radio series "Dixieland Minstrels." Purman moved to Akron in 1940 and became a fixture in the area's amateur theatricals, including producing musicals for the University Club. This script is one of hundreds left among his papers which Mr. and Mrs. T. C. Schaetzle, Jr., donated in 1986. Often adapted by Purman from time-honored routines, they present a vivid recreation of a popular form of entertainment.

170   Tennessee Williams.
The Rose Tattoo.
New York: New Directions, 1951.

The first edition of the revised-for-publication play has been signed by the cast, including Maureen Stapleton, Eli Wallach, and Don Murray. A manuscript draft of the play is in the Robert Lewis papers.

171   Robert Lewis.
"Method — or Madness?"
Typed manuscript.

On April 15, 1957, Robert Lewis, who had gone from the Group Theater to Hollywood and back to Broadway as one its most successful directors, gave the first of a series of eight lectures on the American application of the Stanislavski system of acting. The following year Samuel French published his edited transcripts of the lectures as *Method —or Madness?* The typescript for his influential book is among the papers Lewis began donating to Special Collections in 1990.

172   Arthur Miller.
Autograph letter signed. 1 p. [1962?].

The playwright apologizes to Arthur Lithgow for not being able to see his production of "All My Sons." He writes, "I'd love to know what a current audience in a University made of it." Lithgow, founder of the Great Lakes Theater Festival, donated his papers in 1992.

Item 157

Sheila Smith plays the title role in "Mame" (see item 174).

173 Helene Weigel.
Typed letter signed. 1 p. May 22, 1965.

Director of the Berliner Ensemble following the death of her husband Bertold Brecht, Weigel wrote to Joseph Chaikin giving the company's performance schedule. He had met the actress in East Berlin in the summer of 1962.

174 Lawrence and Lee.
"Mame."
Annotated script. 1966.

This is Sheila Smith's copy marked in red for the character of Mame Dennis and in blue for the character of Vera Charles. Smith, who left Kent State University before graduating for a career on Broadway, understudied Angela Lansbury as Mame and Beatrice Arthur as Vera, for which she won the Theater World Award.

Accompanying her script is a copy of the published script inscribed to her as "Our Ohio wonder-girl" by the authors, Jerome Lawrence and Robert E. Lee, and the lyricist Jerry Herman. It is part of her career archive which she is donating to Special Collections.

175 The Open Theater.
1968–69 Obie.

The Open Theater's award for outstanding achievement off-Broadway for "The Serpent" was signed by Elizabeth Hardwick and the other judges. It is part of the company's archives which began to arrive at the University before it disbanded in 1973.

176 Jean Genet.
Autograph letter signed. 1 p. 1970.

The French playwright asks Marianne du Pury for information about the Black Panthers. This is one of several letters to the composer who worked with Genet when he came to the United States to deliver his 1970 May Day Speech. du Pury, who composed the music for Megan Terry's "Viet Rock" and a song for Jean-Claude van Itallie's "America Hurrah," also worked as an administrator with the Open Theater. Her papers include letters from Edward Albee, Lawrence Ferlinghetti, Allen Ginsberg, Norman Mailer, Anais Nin, and Charles Wuorinen.

177 Judith Malina.
Living Theatre Notebook (1970–71).
Autograph manuscript.

The first of three notebooks by the actress-director, this one describes the company's travels in Brazil and work on "The Favela Piece." Malina and her husband Julian Beck began the Living Theatre in 1949. Joseph Chaikin was a member of the company from 1960 to 1963.

178 Costume Sketch.

Upon hearing of Special Collections's acquisition of the archives of the Great Lakes Theater Festival in 1991, Algesa O'Sickey donated her personal archive of the 1977 production of "The Taming of the Shrew" which she served as costume designer. Shown is her design for the character of Grumio which was played by Tom Hanks.

179 Edward Albee.
Typed letter signed. 1 p. December 4, 1979.

The playwright invites Jean-Claude van Itallie to submit a one-act play for possible production at Lincoln Center. It is from the papers of van Itallie who first visited Kent State University in 1968 and began donating his papers in 1970. He was influential in convincing the Open Theater to deposit the company's archives and Joseph Chaikin to donate his papers. These three interlocking collections form the cornerstone of the department's 20th-century American theater collection.

Science

180 Rembert Dodoens.
A Niewe Herball, or Historie of Plantes . . . .
Antwerp: Printed by Henry Loe for Gerard Dewes of London, 1578.

This is the first English translation of the great 16th-century botanist and physician's popular work. The book contains 875 woodcut illustrations of plants, 30 of which appear for the first time in this edition. It was dedicated to Queen Elizabeth I, and it is reputed to be a source of Shakespeare's information about herbs and other plants.

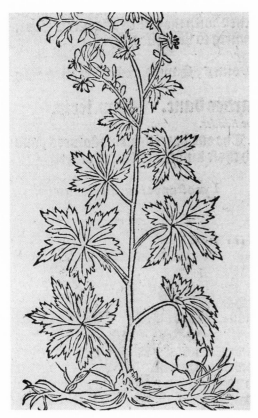

Item 180

Item 181

181   Joannes Kepler.
        Tabulae Rudolphinae.
        Ulm: Jonas Saur, 1627.

This, the first edition of Kepler's last major work, replaced the astronomical tables, known as the *Alphonsine Tables,* that were accepted throughout the 14th and 15th centuries. The data for what became known as the *Rudolphine Tables* were gathered by Tycho Brahe between 1576 and 1596 and were inherited by Kepler upon Brahe's death in 1601. Kepler made some additions and provided analyses and published the data in 1627. The *Tables* remained authoritative for more than a century, thus serving astronomy during the great advances of the 17th century.

This volume was presented to the University Libraries in 1988 by the noted Cleveland collector of books and documents on the development of physical science, mathematics, and technology in the West, John D. Stanitz. It was exhibited, along with 100 other items from his library, in the fall of 1972 in the Department of Special Collections. The exhibit and the catalog that described it were called *Sources of Science and Technology.*

182   Henry David Thoreau.
        Walden; or Life in the Woods.
        Boston: Ticknor and Fields, 1854.

Thoreau's second and final book to be published during his lifetime is an account of the year he spent in a cabin on Walden Pond observing nature. These observations, intermixed with philosophy and classical references, resulted in what is perhaps the most famous nature book by an American. This copy of the first edition is from the library of B. George Ulizio.

183   Charles Darwin.
        On the Origin of Species by Means of Natural Selection, or The Preservation of Favoured Races in the Struggle for Life.
        London: John Murray, 1859.

This is the first edition of what is perhaps the most important book on biology ever written. Darwin's theories on the evolution of man began to develop during the scientist's voyage to South America and Australasia on the "Beagle" in 1831–36. The book was recognized immediately as important and controversial, and it remains so today. This copy is from the libraries of John C. Eckel and B. George Ulizio.

184   Florence Nightingale.
Notes on Nursing: What It Is, and What It Is Not.
New York: D. Appleton and Company, 1860.

This is the first American edition of what has been called "one of the seminal works of the modern world." Written with simplicity, common sense, and wit by the woman who established the professional training of nurses in England and, indirectly, in the United States, the book first appeared in London in 1859 just a few weeks after Darwin's *Origin of Species.*

185   Henry David Thoreau.
Autograph letter signed to James M. Stone. October 11, 1861.

Because of his health, Thoreau regretfully turns down an invitation to provide support for the drive for emancipation of the slaves. This letter, one of the last Thoreau wrote before his death on May 6, 1862, is from the Charles Wesley Slack papers in Special Collections. Slack was a prominent Boston journalist, publisher, and antislavery proponent, and this collection of over 750 letters was presented to the Libraries by one of his descendents, Paul C. Kitchen, Professor Emeritus of Political Science at Kent.

186   Howard E. Jones.
Illustrations of the Nests and Eggs of Birds of Ohio, with Text.
Circleville, OH: n.p., 1879–86.

This collection of 68 hand-colored plates was issued in 23 parts at irregular intervals from July 1879 through December 1886. One hundred sets were planned but only about 90 were actually produced. Although entirely the work of amateurs, the work nevertheless enjoys a high reputation for scientific accuracy and beauty. About this book the distinguished ornithologist Henry Davis Minot wrote, "My enthusiasm has not been so excited for a long while. After careful consideration I can think of no book of natural history in which the beauties of art and of nature are so largely combined." Elliot Coues, perhaps the most severe critic of books on natural history of his time, wrote, "There has been nothing since Audubon in the way of pictorial illustrations of American ornithology to compare with the present work—nothing to claim an equal degree of artistic skill or scientific accuracy," and Casey Q. Wood called it "An outstanding and very rare monograph . . . . The illustrations superb, accurate pictures, drawn from nature." This copy is from the library of Howard Moore of Circleville, one of the original subscribers.

187   H. G. Wells.
Text-Book of Biology.
London: W. B. Clive & Co., 1893. 2 volumes.

H. G. Wells's first book was written while he was a teacher of biology at the University Correspondence College from 1890 to 1892. For the first edition, Wells drew all of the illustrations himself. In 1894, for a revised edition of Part I, the illustrator was A. C. Robbins, one of Wells's students and later his wife. This copy was presented to the Libraries in memory of Professor of Biology Peter J. Zucchero.

188   George W. Crile.
A Bipolar Theory of Living Processes.
New York: The Macmillan Company, 1926.

This volume presents conclusions based upon research that Dr. Crile, one of the founders of the Cleveland Clinic, began in 1898. The book was edited by Amy F. Rowland and this copy is inscribed by Crile for Edna Schnabel.

189   Roger Tory Peterson and James Fisher.
Wild America.
Boston: Houghton Mifflin Company, 1955.

This first edition of an account of a 30,000 mile tour of the continent by two great popularizers of natural history, America's Roger Peterson and England's James Fisher, is from the library of Ralph W. Dexter. Dexter, a longtime professor of biology at Kent State University, an internationally known authority on the chimney swift, and a prolific author of studies in the field of natural history, left his papers to the University Libraries upon his death in 1991. The book is inscribed to Dexter by Peterson.

Miscellaneous

190   George C. Lamb, editor.
The Cryptogram. Volume 1, number 1, February 1932.
Biloxi, MS: The American Cryptogram Association.

A complete run of the official publication of the American Cryptogram Association is held in the Department of Special Collections and Archives as part of the Association's library which is deposited there. Founding editor George C. Lamb, a resident of Burton,

Ohio, developed the journal from a column he wrote for the *Geauga County Leader* called "Secret Corner."

In the summer of 1970, Whiteford C. Bell III presented his collection of books on the subject of cryptography to the University Libraries as a memorial to the founding editor of *The Cryptogram* George C. Lamb. The following year the American Cryptogram Association elected to deposit its library in the Department of Special Collections for the use of their members and for the benefit of the general public.

191   Helen Fouche Gaines.
Elementary Cryptoanalysis: A Study of Ciphers and Their Solution.
Boston: American Photographic Publishing Co., 1939.

This is the first edition of a work sponsored by the American Cryptogram Association and dedicated to George C. Lamb. This copy is inscribed as follows: "To Sis / from / 2 O'clock / and may you understand it / better than I do! / Gelett Burgess / 1939." Burgess was the author of the often-quoted "I never saw a purple cow."

192   Luigi Sacco.
Manuale di Crittografia.
Rome, 1947.

This is the third edition of what is considered to be one of the most important books on cryptography. The first edition, also published in Rome, appeared in 1936. This copy, part of the George C. Lamb Memorial Collection, is inscribed by the author to William J. Bryan of the American Cryptogram Association, September 22, 1947.

193   *Psychedelic Review.* Volume 1, number 1. June 1963.

When Virginia Glenn, "midwife of the human potential movement," died in 1970 her friend Stanley Krippner began the Virginia Glenn Memorial Collection of Readings in Human Potential. Eventually her own papers were added to the collection. Among them were periodicals and offprints representing her wide range of interdisciplinary interests which included world religions, parapsychology, and psychedelic drugs. Her friend Alan W. Watts was among the contributors to the first issue of this magazine.

194   Alan W. Watts.
Typed letter signed. 1 p. January 29, 1971.

In this letter to noted parapsychologist Stanley Krippner, Watts informs him of a memorial tablet which he made for Virginia Glenn. It is accompanied by a photograph. In presenting his papers as part of the Glenn Collection, Krippner included his correspondence with Watts as well as with Charlotte Buhler, Gardner Murphy, and J. B. Rhine.

195   Ira Joel Haber.
[Notebook].
Autograph manuscript. 1970–74.

Among the papers of the artist housed in Special Collections is a notebook full of ideas for sculpture, performance pieces, and writing. Shown is the entry for March 27, 1970: "Series of off-set drawings of trees." In addition to making miniature drawings of the proposed piece, Haber has hand-colored them. The artist also was responsible for the library's securing of the papers of his friend Thomas Richard Wirth which include Haber's 1982 drawing "Mi Californita" and letters from him.

196   Keyes DeWitt Metcalf.
Random Recollections of an Anachronism, or Seventy-Five Years of Library Work.
New York: Readex Books, 1980.

Following the death of prominent librarian Jesse H. Shera, author of *Foundations of the Public Library*, his widow presented his library to Special Collections. Among the volumes was this title, signed by the author who was also a famous librarian. Metcalf was the great uncle of Alicia Metcalf Miller, currently chair of the university's board of trustees. The library published her memoir of Metcalf as part of its Occasional Papers series.

This case from "Ten Plays, An Opera, and A Movie: Moments from the Career of Robert Lewis" features his 1950 production of "An Enemy of the People."

Major Exhibitions in the
Department of Special Collections and Archives

A vital function of any special collections department is the exhibition of its holdings. This gives the public the opportunity to view representative collections. When quarters for such a department in the new Library were designed, appropriate exhibition cases were included in the reading room. The initial exhibition featured strands of Christmas tree lights and cement blocks as part of the work of concrete poet Michael McCafferty. Two decades later a gallery was added which greatly increased the amount of exhibition space. In addition to scholars who come to use the collections for their research, hundreds of visitors annually journey to the 12th floor of the Library to view the exhibitions.

1970

"Words & Objects"
The inaugural exhibition in the department's reading room featured 12 works of concrete poetry by Michael McCafferty. One of the pieces was a sonnet in which words were replaced by the small glass creamers once used in restaurants. The creamers were filled with water; rhymes were indicated by color.
Curator: Alex Gildzen

1971

"Book Binding"
A collection of 19th-century decorative bindings from a private collector were supplemented with fine bindings and books on binding from the Kent holdings. Among the binders whose work were represented were Morrell, Zaehnsdorf, and Riviere & Son.
Curator: Dean Keller

"The B. George Ulizio Collection of English & American Literature"
Of the 1,500 items in the collection, 104 were selected for exhibition. Among those shown were 56 copyright deposit copies, a letter from Mark Twain to Ulysses S. Grant, and an advance copy of Joseph Conrad's *The Rescue*.
Curator: Dean Keller

"AAUP Book Show"
To celebrate the Kent State University Press's membership in the Association of American University Presses, Special Collections mounted this traveling show of the best books of 1970 published by AAUP members.

"Edward Gordon Craig"
Books, prints, and theatrical memorabilia from the private collection of John Wesley Swanson were loaned to Kent. Items included a costume sketch for Craig's 1908 "Hamlet" and a letter from Sir Henry Irving.
Curator: Orville K. Larson

"Lewis Carroll"
The 100th anniversary of *Through the Looking Glass* was marked with an exhibition of the library's Alice in Wonderland collection. In addition to the first edition, items shown included an edition in shorthand, an Alice card game, and numerous translations.
Curator: Dean Keller

1972

"Ohio Authors"
Based on William Coyle's *Ohio Authors and Their Books, 1796–1950,* the exhibition included the manuscript of a philosophical tract by Peter Kaufmann, corrected galley proofs of Robert Lowry's *Casualty,* and first editions of Sherwood Anderson, Christian Cackler, and Paul Laurence Dunbar.
Curators: Alex Gildzen and Dean Keller

"Paul Leichester Ford and Albion Winegar Tourgée: An Exhibition of Their Books from the Personal Collections of Paul Z. DuBois and Dean H. Keller, Supplemented with Books from the Department of Special Collections"
Kent State librarians DuBois and Keller shared their personal collections of 19th century American writers Ford and Tourgée.
Curators: Paul DuBois and Dean Keller

"AAUP 1972 Book Show"
This traveling exhibition of the best books published by members of the Association of American University Presses included a volume from the Kent State University Press, *F. Scott Fitzgerald in His Own Time: A Miscellany.*

"Hart Crane"
Books, manuscripts, and letters of Portage County's greatest poet were exhibited. Included were Crane's letters to Charles Harris.
Curators: Alex Gildzen and Vivian H. Pemberton

"Sources of Science and Technology: An Exhibit of One Hundred and One Books and Documents Showing the Development of Physical Science, Mathematics and Technology in the West"
The first public exhibition of material in the private collection of John D. Stanitz of Cleveland featured the first edition of Isaac Newton's *Philosophiae Naturalis Principia Methematica* and a manuscript of Albert Einstein's that helped lay the foundation for the Unified Field Theory.
Curator: Dean Keller

1973

"Recovering and Preserving the Author's Intention"
The Center for Editions of American Authors marked the sealing of 100 volumes with this traveling exhibition which included the work done at Kent State University on Charles Brockden Brown.

"Bruce Rogers"
Ohio's great book designer and papermaker was spotlighted with an exhibition drawn from the private collection of Robert A. Tibbetts, head of Special Collections at the Ohio State University Library.
Curator: Dean Keller

"Prints by Will Petersen; Books by Frank Samperi"
Throughout his career printmaker Petersen has been a friend of and collaborator with poets. This exhibition included examples of his art and the books of one of the poets with whom he's worked. As part of the exhibition the library sponsored a reading by Samperi and a lecture about his work by Petersen.
Curator: Dean Keller

"Herman Melville"
Special Collections holdings were supplemented by works and artifacts from the private collection of Melville scholar Howard P. Vincent.
Curator: Dean Keller

1974

"100th Anniversary of Robert Frost's Birth"
One of the library's preeminent collections was displayed to mark Frost's centennial. Included were a set of his Christmas booklets and an unpublished photograph of the poet by Lotte Jacobi.
Curator: Dean Keller

"Nathaniel Hawthorne: The College Experience; An Exhibition from the Collection of C. E. Frazer Clark, Jr."
Letters and manuscripts by Hawthorne shared Special Collections' exhibit cases with first editions of his work and six books from Hawthorne's library.
Curator: Dean Keller

"The One Millionth Volume"
Among the nearly 100 items exhibited to celebrate this library milestone were the first book acquired by the Kent State University Library in 1913, John Dewey's *Exposition and Illustration in Teaching* (1910), and the millionth, the A. Edward Newton copy of the first edition, first issue of Walt Whitman's *Leaves of Grass* (1855).
Curator: Dean Keller

1975

"The Feiss Collection"
The cornerstone of the holdings of the Department of Special Collections was some 450 rare books from the private collection of one-time Rowfant Club president Paul L. Feiss acquired by the library in 1952. Several incunables, the second edition of Holinshed's *Chronicles* (1587), and Dickens's *Pickwick Papers* in parts were among the 74 items exhibited.
Curator: Dean Keller

"Kafka"
On exhibit were first editions, translations, bibliographical and biographical studies, and a selection of critical material on Franz Kafka from the private collection of Gary Handler.
Curator: Dean Keller

1976

"Children's Books"
In addition to highlights from the Alice in Wonderland collection, this exhibition included the manuscript of Jacqueline Jackson's *The Taste of Spruce Gum*, original illustrations by Margaret Ayer and Kurt Wiese, a letter from Kate Greenaway, and books described in *From Peter Parley to Penrod*.
Curator: Dean Keller

"Science Fiction and Fantasy"
Books and magazines from the 1940s through the present were on loan from graduate student Michael Tallan.
Curator: Dean Keller

"Ice Skating"
A pair of bone skates more than 700 years old were among the artifacts on display from the private collection of Joseph Butchko. Also shown were prints and photographs of famous figure skaters and a selection from the nearly 150 books Butchko collected over 40 years.
Curator: Dean Keller

1977

"English Literature, 1729–1929"
The first of 85 items in this exhibition was the second edition of Alexander Pope's *The Dunciad,* the last, Robert Bridges's *The Testament of Beauty.*
Curator: Dean Keller

"Rockwell Kent: An Exhibition of Books Written and Illustrated by Kent from the Library of Harry Kamens"
In addition to first and limited editions the exhibition included bookplates designed by Kent and the 1932 *Beowulf* which Kent signed with his thumbprint.
Curator: Dean Keller

"The James Robert Parish Motion Picture Collection"
In 1976 the prolific author of books about the movies donated his personal performing arts research library of more than 600 volumes and 14 boxes of clipping files to the Department of Special Collections. The exhibition included highlights from the gift as well as manuscripts of Parish's books.
Curator: Alex Gildzen

1978

"The Saalfield Publishing Company"
The department acquired the archives of the Akron company in 1977. Among the items in the collection which were displayed for the first time were manuscripts and original art for several of the "Billy Whiskers" books and paper dolls, and coloring books and other items featuring child star Shirley Temple.
Curator: Dean Keller

"John O'Hara"
Matthew J. Bruccoli put together the best-known collection of the work of the popular novelist. When his collection came to Kent, it marked the first public showing of the only known copy of O'Hara's first publication, "The Kungsholm Cruise News," which he edited for the Swedish American Line in 1934.
Curator: Dean Keller

"William Carlos Williams"
Among the 80 items exhibited were portions of the manuscript of *Paterson,* letters from Williams, and notes for a lecture written on one of the poet-doctor's prescription pads.
Curator: Dean Keller

1979

"Book Binding"
The evolution of publisher's binding was traced in this exhibition which included examples of fine bindings in the collection as well as binding tools and supplies.
Curator: Dean Keller

"Father's Day: An Exhibition of Books by Fathers & Children"
Among the books displayed side by side were William Henry Venable's *Floridian Sonnets* (1909) and Emerson Venable's *Poets of Ohio* (1909), Otto Emil Plath's *Bumblebees and Their Ways* (1934) and Sylvia Plath's *Ariel* (1966), and John Barrymore's *Confessions of an Actor* (1926) and Diana Barrymore's *Too Much, Too Soon* (1958).
Curator: Alex Gildzen

"American Bookplates of the 18th and 19th Centuries"
Works by Amos Doolittle, Peter Maverick, and Paul Revere were featured.
Curator: Patricia Kleeberger

1980

"James Thurber"
Over 40 drawings, memorabilia, and manuscripts were loaned from the Ohio State University collection of the Columbus native. Included were drawings removed from an attic wall in Thurber's Connecticut home.
Curator: Dean Keller

"The Lost Art of Letter Writing"
Letters exhibited from the permanent collection included ones penned by John Quincy Adams, Willa Cather, Eugene O'Neill, Marsden Hartley, Frank O'Hara, and James Kirkwood.
Curator: Alex Gildzen

"The Modern Private Press"
The scene was surveyed from England in the last days of the 19th century through current work. Items shown included the Kelmscott Press printing of Chaucer and the Bible printed by the Doves Press.
Curator: Dean Keller

"On the Road: An Exhibition of Beat Writers"
The major publications of William S. Burroughs, Gregory Corso, Lawrence Ferlinghetti, Allen Ginsberg, Jack Kerouac, and Gary Snyder were exhibited.
Curator: Alex Gildzen

"Selections from the Judaica Collection"
Among items exhibited were books from the library of Joseph J. Schwartz (1899–1975), an authority on Semitic literature who served as overseas director of the United Jewish Appeals Joint Distribution Committee during World War II.
Curator: Dean Keller

1981

"The Charles Wesley Slack Papers: A Selection of Letters of 19th Century Authors, Philosophers and Political Leaders"
Slack (1825–85) was an important Boston editor-publisher and state legislator who corresponded with the major figures of his day, including Ralph Waldo Emerson, Henry David Thoreau, Frederick Douglass, Henry James, and Salmon P. Chase.
Curator: Dean Keller

"Across the Gulfs Between the Worlds: Ohio's Contribution to Science Fiction & Fantasy"
In addition to first editions, items in this exhibition included a manuscript by Stephen R. Donaldson and a letter from Leigh Brackett.
Curator: Alex Gildzen

"The Photographer's Art: An Exhibition of Prints & Books on Photography"
Photographs by Lotte Jacobi, Alfred Stieglitz, Imogen Cunningham, Russell Ball, and Doug Moore were interspersed with books about photography and photographers.
Curator: Alex Gildzen

"In the Wind of Wonder: An Exhibition of Selections from the Papers of James Broughton"
Broughton is a poet, playwright, and filmmaker whose papers are housed in Special Collections. Included here were letters to and from Broughton as well as first editions of his books.
Curator: Alex Gildzen

1982

"Lewis Carroll: An Exhibition Marking the 150th Anniversary of His Birth"
The library's Alice in Wonderland collection was the focal point of this exhibition which included pieces formerly in the libraries of prominent Carroll collectors Morris Parrish and B. George Ulizio.
Curator: Dean Keller

"The ESTC at KSU"
The Kent State University Libraries expressed interest in the Short Title Catalog of 18th-Century British Books (ESTC) early in the project. Following the preparation of reports on over 1,000 volumes in the collection, this exhibition brought highlights from these holdings to the public eye.
Curator: Dean Keller

"A Short History of the Movies"
The exhibition opened with the manuscript of the Gerald Mast book whose title it borrowed and included a life mask of actor David Wayne, a costume worn by Doris Day, a 1937 Shirley Temple contract, a book inscribed to Lois Wilson by Bette Davis, and manuscripts of Robert Youngson and James Robert Parish.
Curator: Alex Gildzen

1983

"Dard Hunter and the Making of Paper"
To mark the centennial of one of the leading authorities on the history of paper the department mounted an exhibition of examples of the fine books he printed.
Curator: Dean Keller

"Arkham House/Mycroft & Moran: An Exhibition of Limited Edition Books Published by the Foremost Publisher of Fantasy and Macabre Fiction in This, or Any, Generation"
Kent alumnus Sheldon R. Jaffery loaned items from his private collection of the Wisconsin publisher.
Curator: Dean Keller

"1966–1983: An Exhibition of 100 Significant Books Acquired by the Kent State University Libraries during Hyman W. Kritzer's Tenure as Director"
The exhibition was organized in three sections: English literature, American literature, and a miscellany which ranged from Ohio history to parapsychology.
Curator: Dean Keller

"The Open Theater: A 20th Anniversary Exhibition Drawn from the Company's Archives and the Papers of Joseph Chaikin, Jean-Claude van Itallie, and Marianne de Pury-Thompson"
From the company's organizational statement (1963) through the performance log and program for their final public performance (1973), items in the exhibition recaptured the history of one of the seminal ensembles of the last half of the century.
Curator: Alex Gildzen

1984

"*Black Mountain Review:* A 30th Anniversary Exhibit"
From 1954 through 1957 this influential little magazine was published at Black Mountain College. In addition to the seven issues of the periodical, items in the exhibition included letters from magazine contributors Robert Creeley, Robert Duncan, and Jonathan Williams.
Curator: Denise Cibulas Monbarren

"Charles Brockden Brown's *Edgar Huntley:* The Making of a Critical Edition"
The exhibition traced the evolution and process of preparing the critical edition of the fourth volume in "The Bicentennial Edition of the Novels and Related Works of Charles Brockden Brown" by the University's Bibliographical and Textual Center.
Curator: Nancy Birk

"Tennessee Williams, 1911–1983: An Exhibition of the Work of America's Greatest Playwright"
The majority of the items in the exhibition were from the private collection of Barry V. Daniels.
Curator: Alex Gildzen

"Ars Latina"
The library's oldest book, *Aureola ex Floribus contexta,* was among the items displayed in this exhibition of Latin books.
Curator: Nancy Birk

1985

"Penrod to the Butter Battle"
Twentieth-century American children's literature was featured in an exhibition that sought to continue Jacob Blanck's landmark bibliography *Peter Parley to Penrod.*
Curator: Alex Gildzen

"The 20th Anniversary of the Kent State University Press"
Every book published by the press was exhibited.
Curator: Alex Gildzen

"Masters of 19th Century British Color Printing"
Charles S. Felver of California loaned 58 items from his private collection, including examples of the work of George Baxter and Edmund Evans.
Curator: Nancy Birk

"Huck and the Boys: A Century of Growing Up in American Fiction"
To mark the centenary of the American publication of *The Adventures of Huckleberry Finn* the department mounted an exhibition of books using the initiation theme.
Curator: Alex Gildzen

"Stephen R. Donaldson"
The author of *The Chronicles of Thomas Covenant the Unbeliever* began donating his manuscripts and all editions of his work in 1978. This exhibition traced his career as America's best-selling fantasy writer.
Curator: Dean Keller

"A History of Television"
From autographed covers of *TV Guide* to the manuscript of *Television Drama Series Programming* by Larry James Gianakos, from an early script in the collection of actress Lois Wilson to memorabilia from the papers of veteran television commentator Dorothy Fuldheim, this exhibition attempted to present a historical overview of the medium.
Curator: Alex Gildzen

"A Community of Poets"
Manuscripts and books from eight northeastern Ohio poets were exhibited. The poets were Hart Crane, Collister Hutchison, Ralph Hodgson, Kenneth Patchen, Loring Williams, Langston Hughes, d.a. levy, and Jacob Leed.
Curator: Alex Gildzen

"Nelson Algren: A Comprehensive Look Through the Eyes of a Bibliographer"
Matthew J. Bruccoli assembled a complete collection of the works of this writer for *Nelson Algren: A Descriptive Bibliography* (1985). With the help of the Friends of the Libraries, Special Collections purchased the collection and exhibited highlights.
Curator: Nancy Birk

"The World Publishing Company"
Lillian Zevin, daughter of the founder of the World Publishing Company, wife of the president of the company, and a leading World editor, donated her personal collection of thousands of World titles and the archives of Meridian Books, World's paperback subsidiary. This exhibition featured highlights from her gift.
Curators: Dean Keller and Alex Gildzen

"Charles Clinch Bubb and The Clerk's Press"
This collaboration with the University of Toledo Libraries featured the small books printed by the Cleveland clergyman.
Curators: Richard Oram and Alex Gildzen

"Song & Dance: The 20th Century American Musical"
This exhibition celebrated the University Theatre production of "A Chorus Line" and the Friends of the Libraries lecture by Gerald Mast, author of *Can't Help Singin': The American Musical on Stage and Screen*. It drew heavily from the department's major collection of theatrical programs.
Curator: Alex Gildzen

"2 at 100: Robinson Jeffers, Marianne Moore"
The department commemorated the centennials of two important American poets.
Curator: Alex Gildzen

"Doug Moore: University Photographer"
The first exhibition devoted to the department's archives division featured work of Moore (1924–87), the university's chief photographer for two decades.
Curator: George Hing

"The Spirit Between the Lines: An Exhibition of Translations"
This exhibition featured both English translations from many languages and foreign appearances of English works. In addition to books, the exhibition included the manuscript of Gary Snyder's translation of Han Shan's *Cold Mountain Poems*.
Curator: Dimitris Karageorgiou

1988

"A Woman's Face: Female Iconography in Film"
Six movie actresses were featured in this exhibition which was occasioned by the Women in Film conference sponsored by the Department of Romance Langauges and Literature.
Curator: Alex Gildzen

"UCDA: A Retrospective Exhibition of University & College Design Association Award Winners"
This sampling was taken from the archives of UCDA which are housed in the department.
Curator: Paul Sahre

"High Spots from the Collections of Matthew J. Bruccoli in the Kent State University Libraries"
For two decades the department had acquired books from the library of the editor and bibliographer. On exhibition were examples by Nelson Algren, Raymond Chandler, Stephen Crane, Ring Lardner, John O'Hara, and Kurt Vonnegut, Jr.
Curator: Dean Keller

1989

"Betsy Mix Cowles"
This exhibition from the papers of the 19th-century educator, abolitionist, and advocate of women's rights was mounted to mark the induction of Cowles into the Ohio Women's Hall of Fame.
Curator: George Hing

"Frontiers of the Mind: The Virginia Glenn Memorial Collection of Readings in Human Potential"
Glenn (1931–70) was called "the midwife of the human potential movement." When she died, Stanley Krippner began this collection by donating copies of all his books and articles. Also on exhibit were gifts to the collection from Robert E. L. Masters, Gardner Murphy, and Alan Watts.
Curator: Stephen Leary

"Recent Acquisitions"
Manuscripts from the papers of composer Francesco DeLeone, Melville scholar Howard P. Vincent, and observer of the New York art world Thomas Richard Wirth were exhibited along with a palm-leaf manuscript and a Jan Sobota binding.
Curator: Alex Gildzen

1990

"Virginia Hamilton"
The Newbery Award winning writer began depositing her manuscripts in the department in 1986. This exhibition was opened during the University's 6th annual Virginia Hamilton Conference.
Curator: Kathleen Marten

"May 4, 1990: A 20-Year Retrospective of Response, Reflection, and Remembrance"
The department began collecting materials about the shooting of students on campus immediately following the event. Highlights of two decades of those items were exhibited as part of University-wide anniversary activities.
Curator: Nancy Birk

"The Robert G. Hayman Detective Fiction Collection"
The antiquarian bookdealer started this personal collection as a boy when he subscribed to the popular pulp magazine, *The Shadow*. The department purchased the collection of 800 books and 700 magazines from which this exhibition was drawn.
Curator: Bradley D. Westbrook

"A Gallery of Sinister Perspectives: An Exhibition of Highlights from the Borowitz True Crime Collection"
A new gallery was inaugurated with this major exhibition of items from the newly donated collection assembled over several decades by Albert Borowitz, Cleveland attorney and author of detective novels and books about true crime.
Curators: Alex Gildzen and Bradley D. Westbrook

1991

"From George to George"
This exhibition of presidential materials included the recent gift of autographs from Prof. Harold Schwartz.
Curators: Bradley D. Westbrook and John Brunswick

"Exhibition of Single Sheet Publications"
The art of the broadside exhibits the work of writers, designers, and printers. This showing featured items collected for more than two decades.
Curator: Bradley D. Westbrook

"Ten Plays, An Opera and A Movie: Moments from the Career of Robert Lewis: An Exhibition Selected from His Papers"
This exhibition opened on the night the University Libraries presented the first Robert Lewis Medal for Lifetime Achievement in Theater Research to its namesake.
Curators: Alex Gildzen and Bradley D. Westbrook

1992

"The Art of P. Craig Russell"
The artist loaned some original art to intermingle with copies of his printed work presented in chronological order from his early days with Marvel Comics through his adaptations of operas for the comic book format.
Curators: Brent Kubasta and Alex Gildzen

"van Itallie Hurrah: The Life & Work of an American Playwright"
Beginning with the announcement of Jean-Claude van Itallie's birth, this exhibition featured personal and professional documents of the life of the author of "America Hurrah" and "The Serpent."
Curator: Alex Gildzen

1993

"Maggie & Mudge & May: The Books and Manuscripts of Cynthia Rylant"
As the staff was preparing this retrospective exhibition, the announcement was made that Rylant had won the Newbery Medal.
Curator: Brent Kubasta

"Four Presidents: The Deaths of Lincoln, Garfield, McKinley, and Kennedy"
This look at the assassinations and funerals of the slain presidents was drawn primarily from the gifts of Albert Borowitz, Thomas Cox, and Lillian Sokoll.
Curator: Brent Kubasta

Publications of the
Department of Special Collections and Archives

In order to promote its holdings and services, the Department of Special Collections and Archives has issued a variety of publications. These are listed below, chronologically within the following categories: Exhibition Catalogs, Periodicals, Occasional Papers, Books, Keepsakes, Poems, and Miscellaneous.

EXHIBITION CATALOGS

American Literature. An Exhibition Celebrating the Addition of the 500,000th Volume to the Kent State University Libraries, November 7–December 13, 1968. 1968. Preface by Dean H. Keller.

The B. George Ulizio Collection of English & American Literature. An Exhibition on the Occasion of the Dedication of the Kent State University Library, April 9 & 10, 1971. 1971. "A Note on B. George Ulizio" by Hyman W. Kritzer. Introduction by Dean H. Keller. Designed by J. Charles Walker. 1,000 copies.

Paul Leicester Ford and Albion Winegar Tourgée. An Exhibition of Their Books from the Personal Collections of Paul Z. DuBois and Dean H. Keller, Supplemented with Books from the Department of Special Collections, Kent State University Libraries. 1972.

Sources of Science and Technology: An Exhibit of One Hundred and One Books and Documents Showing the Development of Physical Science, Mathematics and Technology in the West. 1972. Foreword and Introduction by John D. Stanitz. Preface by Bruce Harkness.

Nathaniel Hawthorne: The College Experience. An Exhibition from the Collection of C. E. Frazer Clark, Jr., 16 May through 21 June. . .1974. 1974. Introduction by Hyman W. Kritzer. 500 copies.

The One Millionth Volume: An Exhibition to Celebrate the Addition of the One Millionth Volume to the Kent State University Libraries. 1974. Foreword by Robert I. White. Preface by Dean H. Keller.

The Feiss Collection. An Exhibition of Books from the Library of Paul L. Feiss in the Kent State University Libraries. 1975. "The Paul Feiss Library: A Memoir" by Julian W. Feiss. Preface by Dean H. Keller.

Children's Books. An Exhibition in the Department of Special Collections, Kent State University Libraries, April–June 1976. 1976.

English Literature, 1729–1929. An Exhibition in the Department of Special Collections, Kent State University Libraries, April–July 1977. 1977. Introduction by William Hildebrand.

Rockwell Kent: An Exhibition of Books Written and Illustrated by Rockwell Kent from the Library of Harry Kamens, August 1 through September 30, 1977. 1977.

William Carlos Williams: An Exhibition, October 16, 1978–February 1, 1979. 1979. "Remembering Williams" by David Ignatow. Preface by Dean H. Keller.

Father's Day: An Exhibition of Books by Fathers & Children, June–July 1979. Preface by Paul Metcalf. 26 lettered copies signed by the compiler, Alex Gildzen, and his father.

Display from the Mariana Collection: 163rd Commemoration of the Birth of Baha 'U' Llah, 15 November 1980. 1980.

Across the Gulfs Between the Worlds: Ohio's Contribution to Science Fiction & Fantasy. 27 April–29 May 1981. Cover by P. Craig Russell. 200 copies; 26 lettered copies signed by the artist.

The Photographer's Art: An Exhibition of Prints & Books on Photography. Summer 1981. 1981. "A Note. . ." by Jonathan Williams. Cover photograph of Williams by Doug Moore. 26 lettered copies signed by Williams and Moore.

In the Wind of Wonder: An Exhibition of Selections from the Papers of James Broughton, 26 October 1981–8 January 1982. 1981. "Words before the wind" by Alex Gildzen.

Arkham House/Mycroft & Moran: An Exhibition of Limited Edition Books Published by the Foremost Publisher of Fantasy and Macabre Fiction in This, or Any, Generation. Summer 1983. 1983. Introduction by Sheldon Jaffery.

The Open Theater: A 20th Anniversary Exhibition Drawn from the Company's Archives and the Papers of Joseph Chaikin, Jean-Claude van Itallie and Marianne de Pury-Thompson. November 1983–January 1984. 1983. Preface (1963 journal entry) by van Itallie.

1966–1983. An Exhibition of 100 Significant Books Acquired by the Kent State University Libraries during Hyman W. Kritzer's Tenure as Director of University Libraries, 1966–1983. 1983. Preface by Dean H. Keller. Foreword by Hyman W. Kritzer. Introduction by Matthew J. Bruccoli.

Charles Brockden Brown's "Edgar Huntly": The Making of a Critical Edition, April 9 to June 8, 1984. 1984. Introduction by Nancy Birk.

Tennessee Williams, 1911–1983: An Exhibition of the Work of America's Greatest Playwright. Reading Room, Department of Special Collections, Kent State University Libraries, 18 June–17 August, 1984. 1984.

"Black Mountain Review": A 30th Anniversary Exhibit. 1984. Introduction by Denise D. Cibulas.

Charles Clinch Bubb and The Clerk's Press: The Ward M. Canaday Center, The University of Toledo Libraries, April–June 1986; Special Collections, Kent State University Libraries, September–November, 1986. 1986. Introduction by Robert G. Cheshier. Preface by Richard W. Oram and Alex Gildzen. 500 copies.

Stephen R. Donaldson: An Exhibition, September 16–November 15, 1985. 1985. Catalog Note by Stephen R. Donaldson. Introduction by Dean H. Keller.

The Spirit Between the Lines: An Exhibition of Translations. 30 November 1987–29 January 1988. 1987. Note by Dimitris Karageorgiou, guest curator.

High Spots from the Collections of Matthew J. Bruccoli in the Kent State University Libraries: An Exhibition, 12 September–28 November 1988. 1988. Introduction by Matthew J. Bruccoli. Compiler's Notes by Dean H. Keller.

A Gallery of Sinister Perspectives: An Exhibition of Highlights from the Borowitz True Crime Collection, 11 November 1990–1 February 1991. 1990. Foreword by Jonathan Goodman, Bradley D. Westbrook, editor. 1,000 copies.

Ten Plays, An Opera and a Movie: Moments from the Career of Robert Lewis: An Exhibition Selected from His Papers, 18 November 1991–14 February 1992. 1991. Introduction by Alex Gildzen. 1,000 copies.

The Art of P. Craig Russell. Summer 1992 Exhibition, Department of Special Collections & Archives, Kent State University Libraries. 1992.

van Itallie Hurrah: The Life & Work of an American Playwright. An Exhibition, 19 October 1992–15 January 1993. 1992. 1,000 copies.

Maggie & Mudge & May: The Books and Manuscripts of Cynthia Rylant. Kent State University Libraries, Department of Special Collections and Archives, 16 Feb.–23 April 1993. 1993.

PERIODICALS

The Serif: Kent State University Library Quarterly, Vol. I, April 1964–Vol. XI, Winter 1975. Editor, Dean H. Keller, April 1964–March, 1966; acting editor, Esther Bone, June 1966–June, 1967; editors, Esther Bone and Dean H. Keller, September 1967–December 1970; editors, Alex Gildzen and Dean H. Keller, March 1971–Winter 1975.

Friends of the Kent State University Libraries. Newsletter, Vol. I, No. 1, Spring, 1973–.

OCCASIONAL PAPERS

Wright, Richard. *Letters to Joe C. Brown.* Edited with an Introduction by Thomas Knipp. Preface by Hyman W. Kritzer. First series, no. 1., 1968.

Katz, Joseph. *Rare Books and Very Special Collections.* Preface by Dean H. Keller. First series, no. 2, 1969.

Bennett, Josiah Q. *The Cataloguing Requirements of the Book Division of a Rare Book Library.* Introduction by Hyman W. Kritzer. First series, no. 3, 1969. Second printing, revised and corrected, 1972.

Bruccoli, Matthew J. *Mere Collectors' Items.* Introductory Remarks by Robert I. White, Preface by Hyman W. Kritzer. First series, no. 4, 1969.

Apseloff, Stanford S. *James T. Farrell: A Visit to Chicago.* Introduction by James T. Farrell. First series, no. 5, 1969.

Six Poems/Seven Prints. Alex Gildzen, editor. J. Charles Walker, designer. First series, no. 6, 1971. 500 copies. Poems by John Ashbery, James Bartolino, Gwendolyn Brooks, Denise Levertov, Steven Osterlund, and Gary Snyder. Prints by Grace Hartigan, Alex Katz, Otto Piene, Fairfield Porter, Harve Quaytman, Mary Ann Begland Sacco, and Robert Smithson.

Commager, Henry Steele. *The University and the Community of Learning.* First series, no. 7, 1971. Alex Gildzen, editor. J. Charles Walker, designer.

Grossinger, Richard. *Grossinger's: Two Sections from The Book of the Cranberry Islands.* First series, no. 8, 1972. Cover drawing by Ira Joel Haber. Alex Gildzen, editor. J. Charles Walker, designer.

A Festschrift for Djuna Barnes on Her 80th Birthday. First series, no. 9, 1972. Alex Gildzen, editor. J. Charles Walker, designer.

Commager, Henry Steele. *Individualism, Virtue and the Common Wealth.* Second series, no. 1, 1985. Introduction by Don L. Tolliver. Alex Gildzen, editor. Julia Waida, designer.

Donaldson, Stephen R. *Epic Fantasy in the Modern World: A Few Observations*. Second series, no. 2, 1986. Alex Gildzen, editor. P. Craig Russell, cover. Alex Gildzen and P. Russell Craig, designers.

van Itallie, Jean-Claude. *Calcutta*. Second series, no. 3, 1987. Alex Gildzen, editor. Owen Fabricant, cover drawing.

Miller, Alicia Metcalf. *Library Genes & Other Considerations: A Remembrance of Keyes DeWitt Metcalf*. Second series, no. 4, 1989. Alex Gildzen, editor. Designed & printed in an edition of 500 at The Press at the School of Art (Kent State University)." Wood engravings by Eric May.

Chester, Alfred. *Divertissement De Coin De Rue*. Introduction by Edward Field. Second series, no. 5, 1990. Alex Gildzen, editor.

Borowitz, Albert. *Eternal Suspect: The Tragedy of Alexander Sukhovo-Kobylin*. Second series, no. 6, 1990. Alex Gildzen, editor. Bradley D. Westbrook, copy editor. Harry Kamens, compositor.

Taggart, John. *Prompted*. Poems by John Taggart. Drawings by Bradford Graves. Second series, no. 7, 1991. Alex Gildzen, editor. Bradley D. Westbrook, designer. 500 copies; 26 copies lettered A–Z signed by the author and artist.

BOOKS

Duncan, Robert. *Medieval Scenes, 1950 and 1959*. With a Preface by the author and an Afterword by Robert Bertholf. 1978. 624 regular copies, 100 copies numbered and signed by the author, and 26 copies lettered and signed by the author with a color photograph of the author's illumination for the *Medieval Scenes* papers.

Bowman, George A. *The Importance of Quality Education and Good Teaching: Selected Addresses by George A. Bowman, President of Kent State University, November 18, 1944–July 1, 1963*. Foreword by Phillip R. Shriver. 1979. 500 copies.

Fuldheim, Dorothy. *The House I Live In*. Friends of the Kent State University Libraries Publication Number One. 1980. Julia Waida, designer. 100 copies signed by the author.

Izant, Grace Goulder. *Some Early Ohio Libraries*. Friends of the Kent State University Libraries Publication Number Two. 1981. Julia Waida, designer. 100 copies signed by the author.

KEEPSAKES

Stephens, James. *Behind the Hill: An Adventure of Seumas Beg. A Keepsake for Members of The Rowfant Club, December 6, 1970*. 1970. 50 copies.

Snyder, Gary. *Manzanita, A Keepsake of the Dedication of the Kent State University Library 9/10 April 1971*. 1971. J. Charles Walker, designer.

Mark Twain to General Grant. Department of Special Collections Keepsake. 1973. 200 copies.

Hart Crane to Charles Harris. February 20, 1926. Department of Special Collections Keepsake on the Occasion of the Dedication of a Monument to Hart Crane at Garrettsville, Ohio, November 20, 1978. 1978. 100 copies.

Casale, Ottavio M. *An Unpublished Thoreau Letter. Friends of the Kent State University Libraries Keepsake*. 1979. 500 copies.

Map of the Western Reserve and the Firelands. 1833. Friends of the Kent State University Libraries Keepsake. N.d. 300 copies.

POEMS

Corman, Cid. "Dark Morning. . . ." December 1975. Friends of the Libraries. 400 copies.

Matthews, Jack. "The Landowner Contemplates His Land." November 1976. Friends of the Libraries. 500 copies.

van Itallie, Jean-Claude, "In That Early Time." Published in an edition of 200 copies to celebrate the conferral by KSU of an Honorary Doctor of Humane Letters Degree upon Jean-Claude van Itallie on August 27, 1977.

Broughton, James. "Packing Up for Paradise." December 1977. 600 copies.

Blevins, Richard. "The Death of O." 1978. 350 copies.

Perreault, John. "Alone in Barcelona." 1979. Friends of the Kent State University Libraries. 400 copies.

Bronk, William. "Sizes." 1980. Friends of the Kent State University Libraries. 500 copies.

Anderson, Maggie. "Pine Cone Boogie." Winter Poetry Broadside No. 1. 1990. 1,500 copies.

Beckett, Tom. "Poetry. . . ." 1991. 350 copies; two states, white and gray paper; 26 lettered copies signed by the author.

Harshman, Marc. "January Sixth." Winter Poetry Broadside No. 2. 1991. 1,000 copies.

Blevins, Richard. "American Larch." Winter Poetry Broadside No. 3. 1992. 1,000 copies.

MISCELLANEOUS

Seasonal Greetings. Music from The Polycronicon. Department of Special Collections. December 1972. 150 copies.

Seasonal Greetings. Nativity from the Humanae Salutis Monumenta of Aarias Montanus. Department of Special Collections. December 1973. 100 copies.

Membership Brochures. Friends of the Kent State University Libraries. 1978 and 1991.

Special Collections Handbook. 1978.

Bookmarks. Set of 5. 1981. Reproductions of 3 woodcuts from the Nuremberg Chronicle, 1493; first music printed in England from the Polycronicon, 1495; initial letter "K" from the Kelmscott Chaucer, 1896.

Doug Moore, University Photographer, 14 September–20 November 1987. 1987. Exhibition announcement.

Poster. 1990. The Borowitz True Crime Collection Exhibition. Noel Simms, designer.

Postcards. Set of 5. N.d. Campus scenes: Prof. C. S. Van Deusen in front of Kent Hall; Bookstore across from campus next to the Brady; Blackbird Lake; procession from the "tabernacle"; Reading Room in the Library when it was in the Administration Building.

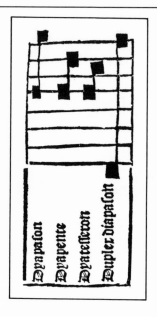

THE FIRST MUSIC
PRINTED IN ENGLAND,
IN THE POLYCRONICON
OF 1495.

DEPARTMENT OF SPECIAL COLLEC-
TIONS OF THE KENT STATE UNIVERSITY
LIBRARIES

*Compliments of the
Friends of the
Kent State University
Libraries*

One of the series of bookmarks
published by the Friends of the
Libraries.

SUBSCRIBERS TO THE 25TH ANNIVERSARY CATALOG
DEPARTMENT OF SPECIAL COLLECTIONS AND ARCHIVES

It is with gratitude that we acknowledge the following donors whose generosity helped make the publication of this catalog possible.

Dorcas Anderson
The Bookseller, Inc.
Geoffrey D. Broadhead
Drs. G. Phillip and Carol A. Cartwright
Mr. and Mrs. Karl G. Chesnutt
DuBois Book Store, Inc.
Dr. and Mrs. Harvey Dworken
Dr. and Mrs. James W. Geary
Al and Helen Kovach Gildzen
Alex Gildzen
Drs. William H. and Ann M. Hildebrand
Janet M. Hoover
Mr. and Mrs. Dean H. Keller
Dr. and Mrs. Gordon W. Keller
Mr. & Mrs. Hyman W. Kritzer
Dr. and Mrs. Sanford Marovitz
L. D. Mitchell
John D. Ong
Charles B. Rosenblatt
Lorie Roth
Mr. and Mrs. John J. Somers
Evelyn Jahn Taub
Dr. and Mrs. Don L. Tolliver
Rose L. Vormelker
Max Weatherly